2.75

JUMP JET
The Revolutionary V/STOL Fighter

Second Edition

"The airplane won't amount to a damn, until they get a machine that will act like a hummingbird — go straight up, go forward, go backward, come straight down and alight like a hummingbird. It isn't easy. . . . Somebody is going to do it."

THOMAS EDISON (1847-1931)

Also available from Brassey's
GODDEN
Harrier: Ski Jump to Victory

HARRISON
Military Helicopters

JUMP JET

The Revolutionary V/STOL Fighter

Second Edition

Bruce Myles

Brassey's Defence Publishers
a member of the Pergamon Group

London · Oxford · Washington D. C.
New York · Toronto · Sydney · Frankfurt

U.K. (Editorial)	Brassey's Defence Publishers Ltd., Maxwell House, 74 Worship Street, London EC2A 2EN
(Orders)	Brassey's Defence Publishers Ltd., Headington Hill Hall, Oxford OX3 0BW, England
U.S.A. (Editorial)	Pergamon-Brassey's International Defense Publishers, 1340 Old Chain Bridge Road, McLean, Virginia 22101, U.S.A.
(Orders)	Pergamon Press Inc., Maxwell House, Fairview Park, Elmsford, New York 10523, U.S.A.
CANADA	Pergamon Press Canada Ltd., Suite 104, 150 Consumers Road, Willowdale, Ontario M2J 1P9, Canada
AUSTRALIA	Pergamon Press (Aust.) Pty. Ltd., P.O. Box 544, Potts Point, N.S.W. 2011, Australia
FEDERAL REPUBLIC OF GERMANY	Pergamon Press GmbH, Hammerweg 6, D-6242 Kronberg, Federal Republic of Germany
JAPAN	Pergamon Press Ltd., 8th Floor, Matsuoka Central Building, 1–7–1 Nishishinjuku, Shinjuku-ku, Tokyo 160, Japan
BRAZIL	Pergamon Editora Ltda., Rua Eça de Queiros, 346, CEP 04011, São Paulo, Brazil
PEOPLE'S REPUBLIC OF CHINA	Pergamon Press, Qianmen Hotel, Beijing, People's Republic of China

Copyright © 1986 Bruce Myles

First edition 1978
Second edition 1986

Library of Congress Cataloging in Publication Data

Myles, Bruce, 1942—
Jump jet.
Includes index.
1. Harrier (Jet fighter plane)   I. Title.
UG1242.F5M95 1985   358.4'3   85–12354

British Library Cataloguing in Publication Data

Myles, Bruce
Jump Jet : the revolutionary V/STOL fighter.
— 2nd ed.
1. Vertically rising aircraft — History
I. Title
623.74'64   TL685
ISBN 0–08–030582–2

Printed in Great Britain by A. Wheaton & Co. Ltd., Exeter

Acknowledgements

I should like to thank the many people both in Britain and America who assisted me in my research and in particular, for their invaluable co-operation, generous background information and research, and general kindness and encouragement — John Godden, John Farley, John Coombs, Taylor Scott and John Fozard.

Contents

PROLOGUE   1

| 1 | GENESIS | 5 |

| 2 | ROLE OF THE HARRIER | 21 |

| 3 | HARRIER AT WAR | 43 |

| 4 | THE LEAP BEYOND THE RIVALS | 65 |

| 5 | THE P1154, A CONTEST WINNER | 99 |

| 6 | THE TRIPARTITE SQUADRON | 115 |

Contents

7   DEVELOPMENT PROBLEMS: SPINNING
     AND SIDE-SLIP   129

8   THE U.S. MARINES ENTER THE STORY   149

9   "THE MOST EFFECTIVE ALL ROUND
     FIGHTER IN EXISTENCE"   181

10   MARINES DISCOVER POWER OF
     THRUST VECTORING: VIFF   207

11   ENGINE PROBLEMS AND SOLUTIONS   227

12   SEA HARRIER DEFIES THE WIND   233

13   THE SUPER-HARRIER: THE HARRIER
     II/AV-8B   261

INDEX   283

Prologue

The flight test airfield of British Aerospace's Kingston-Brough Division is located at Dunsfold, in the undulating, wooded countryside of Surrey, not far from the town of Guildford. One approaches it down a quiet country lane which slips almost unnoticed off the main road to the south coast. The control tower sits as an incongruously small nerve center, dwarfed by the sweep of dark hangars where aircraft are checked before their predelivery test flights. To the right of the tower the fire crew wait in their truck, all day, every flying day, bored with an inactivity which only the unthinkable can relieve.

Like any large airfield cleared of obstructions and wind breaks, a breeze can whip across the openness on the calmest days. The small group of men on the runway on the morning of September 12, 1961, stood close together, collars turned up against just such a breeze. They were there to watch a flight of the company's latest aircraft. It wasn't the first flight, but it was the most crucial. They intended that the lit-

1

tle airplane sitting on the runway would become the world's first operational vertical takeoff and landing fighter. It had already demonstrated that it could hover like a helicopter and fly fast like a normal jet, but the crucial test was now to be attempted. Could it make the transition from this hover into the flight of a conventional jet?

The aircraft itself scarcely looked like the stuff of which aviation dreams are made. It was short, stubby and unpainted with a peculiar undercarriage. There was no sign of a jet tail pipe to exhaust the thrust of the engine. Instead, when the pilot settled in that morning he operated a lever inside the cockpit to swivel two jet exhaust nozzles on either side of the engine. He started the engine, and then pointed the nozzles straight down at the ground.

The men who watched were in a state of suppressed excitement and tension. They were the designers and engineers who'd brought the airplane to this stage. The P1127, as it was called, represented about a million manhours of dedication, frustration and inspiration. It was not some esoteric experiment, but a serious attempt at creating a production prototype. Every man standing there knew that the future of the company could depend on the airplane's success. The aircraft was beginning to rock gently on its undercarriage as the pilot opened the throttle wide for takeoff. The watchers screwed their eyes up against the dust and dug their fingers into their ears as the engine surged into a sustained roar.

The plane lifted smoothly off in an unwavering vertical ascent. Under the rising aircraft the near horizon shimmered into a blurred outline through the translucent columns of jet exhaust from the four nozzles. The swirling heat beat against the watchers' faces for a few seconds, then the nozzles swivelled slowly towards the rear, edging backwards against the side of the fuselage. Immediately, the little airplane started moving forward from the hover. It gathered speed in a surge of acceleration and streaked off into conventional flight.

The prototype disappeared from sight and the receding engine note rose and fell over the airfield in an irregular wash of sound. As it faded, the men on the ground burst quite spontaneously into a long, sustained cheer. It was an extraordinary spectacle for a group of supposedly unemotional Englishmen. However, that cheering was the uninhibited expression of triumph for an airplane which was to revolutionize the concepts of tactical airpower and signal the advent of a whole new breed of aircraft. Here was an aircraft as revolutionary as the jet engine itself.

This is the story of that aircraft.

Chapter 1

Genesis

The story of the Harrier starts back in the mid-1950's. Its genesis was rooted not in success, but in failure—the failure of another airplane. It was that failure which gave the designers of the Harrier the time and the incentive to make the breakthrough into the world's first operational vertical takeoff and landing fighter.

In 1954 Hawker Aircraft Limited (part of Hawker Siddeley Group), in a design competition for a supersonic fighter for the defense of the United Kingdom specified F155T. Hawker's contender was the P1103, a single engine, Mach Two-plus interceptor fighter which in the end of the day lost out to the Fairey Aviation contender, a souped-up version of the Fairey FD2 which previously had held the world's speed record. This Fairey fighter was later scrapped, but the losers of that contest, Hawker, decided that all the design effort they had put in should not be wasted.

The Royal Air Force was looking ahead to a replacement for the Hawker Hunter ground attack fighter. Hawker designers, looking at the mock-up of the P1103, decided to use that as the basis for a new supersonic interceptor/interdection, strike and close support aircraft. The Royal Air Force's Air Staff had not yet crystallized their thoughts on the form of the replacement. The Hawker Board reasoned that if they could get a prototype flying quickly, they could help make up the Air Staff's minds for them. They poured about a million pounds worth of design effort into the project. Their subcontractors on undercarriage, and other components, spent about the same.

The new fighter, type-numbered P1121, was about 85 percent structurally complete and had become the company's great hope for the future when disaster overtook them. Defense Minister Duncan Sandys in his famous 1957 Defense White Paper, "Statement on Defence," declared that manned fighters would no longer be necessary, and that missiles could do their job from now on. There was still to be a requirement for a new manned bomber which hardened into the Air Staff's Operational Requirement OR 339, known better by the design eventually built to meet it, TSR 2.

The P1121 was doomed. But Hawker had spent around a million pounds of their own money, and they made one final effort to salvage the project. Design studies were made of variants of the P1121, including one that was a very extensive redesign giving it two engines and two seats. It was clear that it was not going to meet the requirements of OR 339. They called it "the poor man's TR 2." This was a wry reference to the ambitious scale of the successful contender, the British Aircraft Corporation's Tactical Strike and Reconnaissance aircraft. It was little consolation to Hawker Siddeley that the TSR 2 was later to founder itself, the victim of one of Britain's biggest political rows in years.

Hawker, under their Chief Designer, Sir Sydney Camm, had been accustomed for many years to designing fighter aircraft for the Royal Air Force. It is said that Sir Sydney went to the Chief of the Air Staff every year or so with a new design, and the C.A.S. would look at it and say, "Yes, jolly nice, Sydney. I think we'll have a hundred of those." The story may be apocryphal, but the situation was almost literally like that. The Hawker tradition had been one of private development with an almost assured market at the end of it all. When the Board of Directors gritted their teeth and took the decision to cease work on the P1121, Hawker realized that a new, harsher era had dawned. The highly successful Hunter was still being sold all over the world in large numbers, so there was no immediate financial problem. However, an aircraft company flourishes on new initiatives and the demise of the P1121 left a large vacuum in the activities of the design office. This was the spur which led them down the road to vertical takeoff and landing.

It is ironic that, had the 1121 gone on and into production for the Royal Air Force, there is absolutely no doubt in the minds of those who had been involved at that time that the company's interest in vertical takeoff and landing would have died there and then. Many of the people who were later to become such enthusiasts for the vertical takeoff and landing aircraft, would have sighed with relief to be able to concentrate on the P1121, a straightforward, conventional airplane. When one considers that Hawker Siddeley is the only company to succeed in turning out a production VTOL aircraft, it's a fascinating hypothesis to consider how far along the road to vertical takeoff and landing the world of aviation would have progressed by now.

British aircraft companies, unlike their American counterparts, have never followed a policy of hiring design and development staff to get them over a peak, and then firing them again. At Hawker Aircraft Ltd. (HAL), now part of British Aerospace, the philosophy had always been to keep a steady modest-sized permanent design staff whose task was to keep initiating new projects in a continuous, self-fulfilling cycle. At

The partially completed first prototype of the ill-fated Hawker P1121 whose cancellation in 1958 was the spur to the development of the P1127.

the height of the P1121 project, about a third of the 450 design staff were working on that airplane. When the writing started to appear on the wall concerning the P1121, the pressure was on to generate new projects. Ralph Hooper, new Chief Engineer at Hawker Siddeley Kingston, was then a young project designer, and one afternoon a brochure for a new engine with swivelling jet nozzles landed on his desk. As he read it, his pulse quickened, and he started to make some calculations. A few hours later he had finished sketches of an airplane which can clearly be recognized as the forebear of today's Harrier.

One cannot separate discussion of the Harrier from its engine, and one cannot discuss the engine without giving credit to two men; one, a small, crippled Frenchman, and the other a large, extroverted American. The Frenchman was Michel Wibault, a well-known aircraft designer and the American is General Willis Chapman. Chapman, then a Colonel, was head of a mutual weapons development group based in Paris. This group of American officers had been given a large sum of dollars to help develop weapons of interest to NATO, but which weren't being supported by the appropriate NATO governments. It wasn't pure altruism — clearly there were going to be benefits to the U.S. forces as well. And the Mutual Weapons Development Program would play a crucial part in the engine development.

Sir Stanley Hooker was Technical Director of the Bristol Aero Engine Company back in the mid-1950's. His association with the MWDP had started with the Bristol Orpheus engine which he designed for the Fiat G91 NATO light fighter. The American group funded three-quarters of that engine's development, and during that period, Hooker, a cheerful extrovert, formed a friendship with Colonel Chapman. From a light fighter, it seemed natural to talk about vertical takeoff. However, at that time, most of the talk was of aircraft with separate engines for vertical lift-off and landing which would be shut down while other engines took over the propulsion in conventional flight. Rolls Royce, at Derby, who were later to merge with the Bristol Aero Engine Company, were already flying this combination of engines in the Short SC1 research prototype fighter. Hooker concedes now that he had given very little thought to any other means of vertical takeoff and landing.

Within a very short time, his friend, Colonel Chapman arranged a meeting which set him off down a new and exciting road. Chapman recalled the conversations on vertical takeoff when, early in 1957, Michel Wibault came to him to ask for support for his Gyroptere, a single seat fighter. The Gyroptere had a single engine in the fuselage with four centrifugal compressors, two on each side, driven by cross shafts and gear boxes. The little airplane took off and landed vertically by rotating the scrolls of the centrifugal blowers downwards, and flew conventionally by pointing them rearwards. Chapman invited Hooker to Paris to listen to Wibault's "presentation" of the Gyroptere. Hooker thought the system was very complicated, but he was excited by Wibault's basic concept of rotating the thrust. It seemed that this rotation could be done without much power and that based on the proven Orpheus engine, this rotation of thrust for vertical lift had strong potential. Stanley Hooker's brilliant reputation in world aviation is based to some extent on his almost intuitive approach to engineering. He flew back to England, his mind racing with ideas for a new engine.

Hooker and his team at Bristol produced a brochure for an engine called the BE53, later to become the Pegasus. It had one swivelling jet nozzle either side which would lift an aircraft off vertically and then propel it forward by swivelling the nozzles rearwards. The engine used the well-proven Orpheus as the central core, combined with two stages of the low pressure compressor from an Olympus engine. It was an integrated device, without Wibault's complicated drive shafts. The air was drawn in through two holes at the front, and the air passing through the Olympus fan was ducted through the two swivelling nozzles. The air for the Orpheus part went straight out of a hole in the back.

Bristol started hawking their brochure around the various airframe companies. Sir Sydney Camm had already had a peremptory look at the brochure at the 1957 Paris Air Show at Le Bourget. It now landed on his desk officially followed by a famous, typically terse note to Stanley Hooker which read: "Dear Hooker, what are you doing about V/STOL?, Yours sincerely, Camm." On closer inspection of the brochure, Sir Sydney thought that with the thrust it was offering (around 11,000 pounds), it was little better than a joke. It certainly didn't seize his imagination at that stage, and drifted downstairs to the project office where young Ralph Hooper picked it up that afternoon. Hooper was, in his own words, "browned off" by the lack of creativity and the general air of despondency surrounding the seemingly-inevitable rundown of the P1121 saga. No one actually told him to study the brochure, but after looking at it for about an hour he became completely absorbed.

Here was the basis of a beautifully simple idea for vertical takeoff and landing. Much less complicated than multi-lift and cruise engine machines like the Short SC1. On a piece of paper he started sketching, wrapping an airframe around the engine. From the thrust available, it looked as if the aircraft would use a short takeoff technique followed by a vertical landing. But thrust was so limited that a military load seemed impossible. That first sketch was of a three seat aircraft which might be used for liaison duties on the battlefield, but a quick calculation of weight showed that even that limited objective was unlikely, so he sketched a two seater next. Although it was not very pretty, it looked purposeful. The genesis of today's airplane can be seen in that rough drawing, hurriedly sketched out that afternoon.

Bristol had not suggested deflecting the thrust from the Orpheus part of the engine at the back end. This seemed very wasteful to Hooper, because if one didn't deflect the thrust from both ends and allowed some of it to belch out of the back, one was denying an aircraft all the available power for vertical takeoff and landing. John Fozard, now chief designer of Harrier, was Project Engineer on the doomed P1121 project at that time and shared an office with Ralph Hooper. Fozard was still deeply involved in the airplane, but he kept sneaking a glance over Hooper's shoulder at the intriguing doodles and calculations that littered his desk. They and a few others tossed ideas around and hit on the scheme of splitting the jet pipe (as Hawker had done on the Sea Hawk jet) to add two swivelling nozzles which would deflect the rear thrust as well. The sketches began to look better and better. But it was a radical thing to do to the engine and Bristol was not too pleased. The first reaction was "impossible." Then after realizing their past success at high temperature engineering, they relented. They also changed the nozzles from the clumsy bent elbow type to the neat cascade nozzles of the present day engine.

It was all fairly low key at this stage. Hawker still hoped that their variants on the P1121 would somehow win through. Then cancellation came, and in the absence of anything else to do, a slow but steady increase in design effort was brought to bear on this strange little V/STOL—vertical/short takeoff and landing—project. There was a hard core of enthusiasts for the concept. At first Sir Sydney Camm was not numbered amongst them. To understand why, it is necessary to know a little about this man who had been a dominant figure in British aircraft manufacturing for many years.

Sir Sydney, who was knighted in 1953, had been Chief Designer of Hawker Aircraft since 1925. He retained that position until his death in 1966, and during that time, he produced fifty-two types of aircraft of which over 26,000 had been made. It is an unequalled record and a tribute to a man who has been described by some as the greatest Chief Designer of military aircraft during this century. From his era, until now, there has never been a time without a Hawker aircraft in front line service with the Royal Air Force. He is remembered not only with immense respect for his brilliance as an engineer and designer, but with real affection by most who came in contact with him.

He was a natural, an intuitive engineer. A man with little formal education, Sir Sydney came up from the bottom. Beginning as a carpenter in the First World War, he ascended through the drawing office to his present eminence by sheer ability and hard work. Though he never questioned the efficacy of lifting off the ground vertically, his naturalistic tendencies almost recoiled from the mechanical embodiment of these principles. Sir Sydney had not been trained like modern engineers to think and look ahead. In fact, his skepticism lingered for a long time, until the flight test program was well under way. At the back of his thoughts was always a deep regret about the cancellation of the P1121. He saw it as the supersonic successor to the beautiful Hunter. There is no doubt that the P1121 might well have mopped up the overseas markets which the Phantom and the French Mirage went on to dominate.

Sir Sydney Camm (center), the famous Hawker Chief Designer, talks with Bill Bedford (right), then Chief Test Pilot, shortly after the first conventional flight of the P1127 at the Royal Aircraft Establishment, Bedford, England, March 1961.

Sir Sydney was a perfectionist and a stickler for detail in everything he did. Two of his main hobbies were cycling and golf. He was constantly putting forward improvisations for lightweight cycle designs. On the golf course, partners would be treated to detailed and often amusing dissertations on the design of golf clubs, their moments of inertia, their angles of loft. His approach to golf was the same as his approach to work—a constant striving for improvement. Throughout his career his working day would start with a storm through the cavernous office, pausing here and there to peer at someone's work. If it did not appear to reach his required standards, he would snort, "It looks as if mother did it." However, even Sir Sydney's morning forays through the apprehensive ranks of drawing boards could not possibly take in every aspect of the design work. He used to lament, "There's a future disaster issued every day."

He was a great team leader and remained so until his death in 1966. Although the great man had little to do with the actual design of the aircraft which was to become the Harrier, the bright young men who designed it had been chosen by him. Sir Sydney had an almost unerring eye for talented people and saw the importance of graduate trainees before any of his contemporary chief designers. However, as the P1127—as the new project had been christened—got under way there were some who felt that his constant skepticism, a deliberate tactic he had used for years to draw the best from people, no longer had the bite it once had. Rarely now did it evoke the old response of making another man question his own thinking towards the problem on the drawing board.

The Hawker tradition, which Sydney Camm had done so much personally to forge, was one of conservatism. His dictum had always been, "Let's do the best we can within known and fairly conventional technology." It had been an extraordinarily successful tenet up until then. The highly successful Hawker Hunter fighter was a typical example. It was

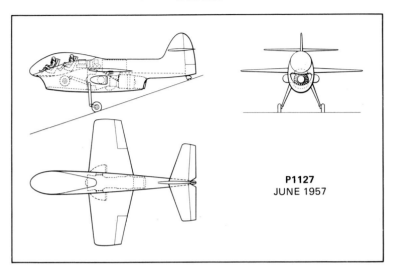

P1127
JUNE 1957

the acme of conventional swept wing aerodynamics and did not embody a single new principle that had not already been used in any other new jet airplane. It had a single engine, it had bifurcated intakes, and it had a swept wing and a swept tail. However, the Hunter did it with all the flair and skill that the very experienced Hawker team could provide at that time. Now though, as the peak of Hunter production began to tail off, the P1127 was the only new project which the company had. Camm was faced with little choice but to press on with this new airplane which was not only new in concept, but completely revolutionary. It made him nervous and apprehensive, and this manifested itself in skepticism at every opportunity.

One of his pet hates was the unusual undercarriage which embodied outrigger wheels on the wingtips. He used to stump around long after the airplane was flying successfully muttering, "They'll break off like bloody carrots I tell you." Ralph Hooper spent a long time trying unsuccessfully to persuade him that it was not really any different from a flying

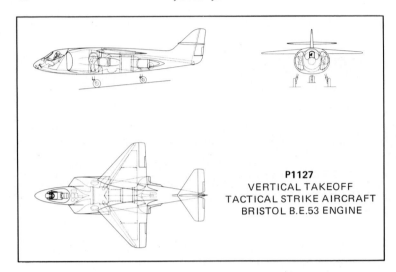

P1127
VERTICAL TAKEOFF
TACTICAL STRIKE AIRCRAFT
BRISTOL B.E.53 ENGINE

boat's floats, and they did not snap off, even when they landed on rough water. It was all to no avail. Camm had once encapsulated this marvellous belief he had in his own rightness in the words, "You know, the only time I'm wrong is when I'm persuaded against my better judgment."

Some people regarded the "old man" as nothing more than a nuisance as he leaned over their shoulder peering at this feature or that on the drawing board, vowing that it would only go into the new aircraft "over my dead body." What irritated some was that he would rarely give a rationale for his objections. His forays through the drawing office had one profound effect: they made sure everyone had done his homework, just in case Sir Sydney should fix his eye on someone and demand an explanation of some detail. Sir Sydney was, after all, still the Chief Designer. No matter how he chivvied his design teams in private, in public he would defend them to the end. It was hardly surprising that he commanded such loyalty from his team.

The engine of any new aircraft has to start in advance of the airframe if they are going to come together in time to fly.

So, although Hawker was able to finance design study work fairly cheaply for the first part of their collaboration with the Bristol Engine Company, the engine makers needed a big injection of cash quickly. Early in 1958 Stanley Hooker flew back to his friend Colonel Chapman at the MWDP office in Paris. People like Chapman, and a few far-sighted military men in NATO were beginning to have stirrings of unease about the vulnerability of conventional long runways in any future conflict. There was clearly a background of interest in V/STOL proposals, but Hooker was talking in terms of millions of dollars. Despite his good relationship with Colonel Chapman, he needed every bit of extra support he could muster. It came, out of the blue, in the form of another member of that apparently limitless club of aeronautical extroverts, a famous professor called Theodore von Karman.

Von Karman was a Hungarian Jew who had been Professor of Aeronautical Engineering at Aachen in Germany in the early 1930's. He was a tremendously likeable man and extremely clever, although his academic brilliance never stopped him carousing and singing with his students until the early hours. When he and Hooker met at Cambridge University in 1934, where they were both doing research on supersonic aerodynamics, they got along famously. Von Karman saw the signs in time, got out of Hitler's Germany and played a big part in rocket development. Over the years he became the effective "Dean of Aeronautical Science" in the United States. Hooker had seen him from time to time, over the years, on trips to the United States, and now von Karman had been appointed Chairman of Aircraft Research and Development in Europe, working closely with MWDP. In fact, the young officers relied on von Karman's "thumbprint" on their proposals to encourage Washington to sanction them. To Hooker's delight, von Karman came in on the discussions on this new vertical lift engine which Bristol would christen the Pegasus. Von Karman looked at the drawings and pointing at the configuration of the swivelling nozzles exclaimed, "Ah, vectored thrust!" This was the first time anyone had used the expression to describe the potential of the engine to change the direction of its thrust, and it's been used ever since.

With von Karman's active support, Chapman's office supplied the first of about ten million dollars support money for engine development. Their contribution was 75 per cent, with the rest coming from Bristol's own funds. The program was initially for six engines, four for bench testing and two for flight. Sir Stanley, with great largesse, came back and allocated the flight engines to Sir Sydney for the 1127 program. On his way out from Sir Sydney's office the chilling realization crept over him, "They're not my engines; they belong to MWDP." He persuaded Chapman to visit the Hawker factory at Kingston on Thames near London. The American's reaction was, "Of course, Hawker can have the flight engines." The enthusiasm, the interest, the generosity of the Americans, through their MWDP office, cannot be overstated. If it were not for them, there would not have been an engine, and without the engine there would have been no airplane. That initial support was the start of a powerful American connection in the Harrier story. This is a thread which runs through to the present day, and the U.S. Marine Corps' commitment to the airplane, and its undoubted future influence on U.S. Naval aviation in general.

There is a story which typifies the attitude of the Americans in those early days, their faith in the engine, and their reaction to honest, straight dealing. A team of experts from Wright Field, the U.S.A.F. research and development test center, summoned Stanley Hooker to Paris to talk about some of the early problems he was having on this project, into which they were pouring so much money. They were a pretty uncompromising looking bunch seated around the table, but Hooker took a deep breath and decided to tell them the unvarnished truth about the engine deficiencies, without any undue optimism about the speed with which he could solve the problem. When he sat down at the end of his exposition, the other members of the Bristol team muttered out of the corners of their mouths that he had ruined their case, and that the project would be cancelled out of hand. The chairman stood up and told Hooker, "That's the frankest exposition of an engine we've ever heard. I've only got one more question to ask. How much money do you want to complete the job!"

Sir Stanley Hooker admits that he always "violently underestimated" the cost of the engine development, but the MWDP never reneged on their agreement to pay 75 per cent of the continuing cost, until Britain's Ministry of Defense gradually assumed responsibility. The first Pegasus engine ran on the factory test bench at Bristol in September 1959, and the first flight engine was delivered to Hawker one year later. It was an extraordinarily speedy development.

As we will see, despite or perhaps because of its revolutionary nature, the proponents of this unique airplane had an uphill struggle to convince many of the people who mattered that it was a viable concept. During its development, Stanley Hooker was required by Sir Sydney to appear at his office in Kingston every Monday morning at ten o'clock. One day he greeted the engine designer with, "Well, have you got a sufficient sense of grief and shame?" Hooker racked his brains in vain for any disaster of the preceding week. Camm continued, "You come here every Monday, spending the country's money on this harebrained scheme of vertical takeoff. Have you no sense of shame about it?" Then he grinned. It was Sir Sydney's nature that the more the Establishment frowned on it, the more he defended the little airplane his company had pinned its hopes on.

Chapter 2

Role of the Harrier

The Pegasus engine, the heart of the Harrier, is unique for several reasons, one being that it is designed specifically for the aircraft which uses it. That is not a truism, because most jet engines are developed as a completely separate power unit for whichever aircraft chooses to use it. Some engines power a number of different airplanes, but with the Pegasus you simply could not design another airplane around it. Rolls Royce discovered this when they tried to drum up some more business for the engine a few years ago by showing it to some American aircraft firms. Several looked at it carefully, and there's no doubt they did a few drawings around it. Then their interest abruptly faded. There was no public statement, but it is almost certain that the airplane they sketched around the Pegasus looked like a carbon copy of the Harrier. And who was going to spend money producing another Harrier ten years after Hawker?

The Pegasus is similar in principle to the fan jet engines which now power many of the world's latest airliners. Its means of achieving VTOL is called vectored thrust, von Kar-

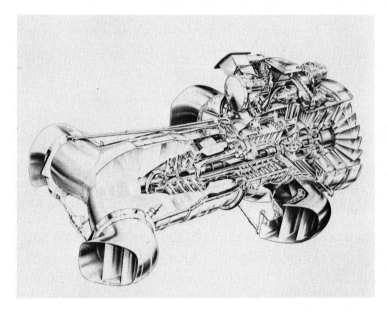

Cutaway drawing of the Rolls Royce Pegasus 11 vectored thrust turbofan engine which is rated at 21,500 lb. static thrust and powers the Harriers at present in service with the Royal Air Force, the U.S. Marine Corps, the Spanish Navy, the Royal Navy and the Indian Navy as Pegasus 104.

man's expression, because the pilot can change both the length and the direction of the thrust vector. In simple terms, it is a turbofan engine in which the air passes through the fan or low pressure compressor and then divides. Less than half the air then goes through the high pressure compressor, the combustion system and the turbine to form the hot stream. The remainder, the cold stream, flows over the outside of the high pressure compressor. Now, in a normal type of turbofan engine, the cold stream is blown aft by the fan through a tail-pipe into the atmosphere. In the Pegasus, the cold stream is exhausted through the two front nozzles on either side of the engine, and the hot stream through the two rear nozzles. All four are mechanically linked together and can be directed downwards for vertical takeoff, aft for conventional flight, or to intermediate positions for short takeoff and slow landing.

After much trial and error, the engine and airframe designers reached a compromise between the center of gravity of the aircraft, and the center of thrust from the four rotating nozzles. As the nozzles are rotated, the line of action of the thrust always passes through the center of gravity of the aircraft with the result that there is no pitch change on the aircraft as it accelerates from vertical takeoff to wingborne flight. We will look some more at this problem of center of gravity later.

Another important feature pioneered on the Pegasus also helped in control in the hover. The two compressor/turbine systems—the high pressure and low pressure—rotate independently. They have been designed to turn in opposite directions to eliminate a gyroscopic effect which has plagued the handling of other attempts at V/STOL aircraft. If present, this gyroscopic effect means that when the aircraft is pitched, it yaws and when it is yawed, it pitches. The engine is controlled by pouring more or less fuel into the combustion chamber, where it is injected into the compressed air and burned.

One of the important auxiliary features of the engine is its gas turbine starter which makes engine starting entirely independent of any ground trolley aids. John Dale, the Pegasus Chief Engineer, was sitting beside an American senator at a flying demonstration waiting for the Harrier to start up and take off. The senator leaned across and said, "Let's get this show on the road. Where's the starting trolley?" The last two words were almost drowned out as the pilot, clearly blessed with some sixth sense, pressed the button and the Pegasus roared into life!

Now, given the engine that can do the job, what are the principles governing vertical takeoff and landing? They're the same as those that govern any vertically moving device, whether it is a balloon, airship or Harrier. The weight is overcome by an equal and opposite force. In the case of the balloon or airship, lift is provided by gas, hot air or helium. The Harrier lifts off because the thrust of the Pegasus exceeds the weight of the aircraft. The nozzles are pointed down vertically, the throttle is opened and daylight appears under the wheels, as it leaps into the air. But, it will not continue upwards in a smooth vertical rising path because that way it is a naturally unstable flying machine.

Conventional aircraft have moveable surfaces controlled by movements of the stick and rudder pedals. There is the rudder for directional control, the elevator to control pitch, and ailerons on the wing surfaces for roll control. The Harrier in vertical flight has no airstream passing over these control surfaces so another system had to be devised. Known as the jet reaction control system, it takes air from the engine and ducts it through lightweight pipes to special valves or "puffers" at the nose, tail and each wing tip of the aircraft. As the pilot moves the control column and rudder in the hovering mode, he opens and shuts these puffers at the corners of the Harrier. A very high velocity jet of high pressure air comes out, and the traditional rules of Sir Isaac Newton come into play—an action and reaction being equal and opposite. The pilot generates a force up at one wing tip and down at the other to control the aircraft in roll. He pulls the stick back and the valve at the nose opens and pitches the nose up. This reaction control system comes into operation automatically, when the pilot selects the engine nozzles down from the horizontal position they normally occupy in conventional flight, to point towards the ground for V/STOL movements.

Sitting side by side at the pilot's left hand are the nozzle selector lever and the throttle. The concept of controlling the thrust vector was that the throttle would control the length of the thrust vector (the amount of thrust you get), and the nozzle lever would control the direction of the thrust vector. The nozzle lever has always been regarded by the designers as much of a "go faster" lever as the throttle. When the nozzles are vertical, the lever is essentially upright in the cockpit. If you push it forward the nozzles rotate backwards, and of course, as the jet gases pour rearwards the nozzle lever has acted as a "go faster" control.

Conventional aircraft throttle movements tend to be comparatively coarse, but during control in the hover, the Harrier requires delicate movements to maintain height accurately. So, a wrist support was fitted just above the throttle lever to help the pilot get fine control. Incorporated in the throttle lever is the engine "re-light" button, airbrake switch and "press-to-transmit" radio switch. There is a fixed vertical takeoff stop to which the pilot can move the nozzle lever without looking down. The lever is spring loaded and for free and gradual movement during transitions he simply lifts the lever up, overriding the stop. A United States Air Force test pilot in 1969 paid the system a compliment, stating, "It's so simple, so elegant. It sets the standard against which every future V/STOL control must be measured."

Once the aircraft is off the ground vertically and the pilot is controlling its flight path away from the ground, he then starts to rotate the nozzles aft. There are limits to how quickly he can do this. If he's sitting at fifty feet and is foolish enough to slam the nozzles rearwards, which could be done in around a third of a second, then, once again, Sir Isaac Newton would dominate. The airplane would drop like a stone. Self-preservation is a compelling instinct, so the pilot rotates the nozzles initially around ten to twenty degrees from the vertical. He maintains height but has immediately started accelerating forward by a third or quarter of a G. He continues then to progressively rotate the nozzles backwards

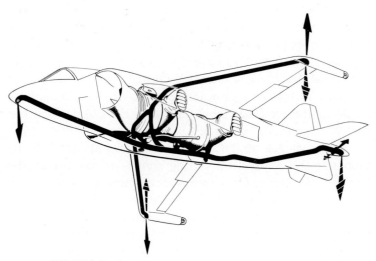

JET REACTION CONTROL SYSTEM

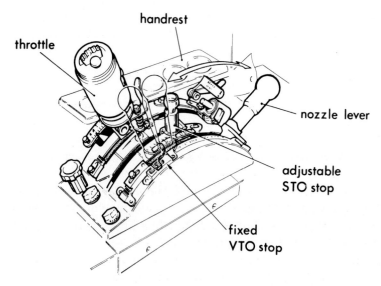

throttle

handrest

nozzle lever

adjustable
STO stop

fixed
VTO stop

NOZZLE SELECTOR LEVER

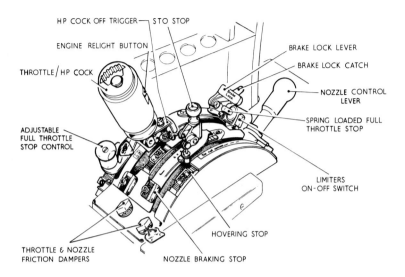

HP COCK OFF TRIGGER — STO STOP
ENGINE RELIGHT BUTTON
THROTTLE / HP COCK
ADJUSTABLE
FULL THROTTLE
STOP CONTROL
THROTTLE & NOZZLE
FRICTION DAMPERS
NOZZLE BRAKING STOP
HOVERING STOP
BRAKE LOCK LEVER
BRAKE LOCK CATCH
NOZZLE CONTROL
LEVER
SPRING LOADED FULL
THROTTLE STOP
LIMITERS
ON-OFF SWITCH

CONTROLS

until, after about fifteen or twenty seconds he's gained sufficient airspeed—around 160 knots—for the aircraft to be flying conventionally on its wings and no longer dependent
upon the downward thrust. With the nozzles horizontal for
conventional flight, the reaction control system has been
automatically switched off, and the conventional control surfaces are operating like any other jet.

The decelerating transition or return to the hover from
conventional flight is the exact reverse. The pilot approaches
his desired landing point, and at some convenient distance,
typically perhaps a mile down wind of it, while flying at
around 200 knots, moves the nozzles past the vertical position to the reverse thrust stop. This gives him about twenty
degrees of forward thrust vector rotation. Immediately, the
aircraft will start to slow down and in this process the wing
generates less lift. So, with the nozzles fixed in the so-called
braking stop, the pilot applies more power. Within about

twenty seconds the aircraft has lost around 200 knots of airspeed and replaced aerodynamic lift on the wings with engine
thrust. This decelerating transition will have taken the pilot
only about half a mile.

Pilots say the Pegasus engine is the world's best airbrake.
Once the aircraft hovers conveniently over the landing spot,
the pilot merely takes off a little bit of throttle, and the aircraft starts to descend. When the wheels hit the ground, he
throttles back, swivels the jets aft and taxis off. If the landing
spot is obstructed, the pilot can tilt the aircraft like a helicopter, even with the nozzles in the VTO position, and "trans-
late" it over distances of up to half a mile in half a minute to
a more convenient landing spot. Half a minute in hovering
flight consumes around eighty pounds of fuel, so the pilot
has great freedom during the landing phase.

There is a very apt Harrier pilot's aphorism, "Far better
to stop and land, than land and try to stop." There's another
analogy: the energy of a modern fighter landing conventionally on a runway is equivalent, in destructive energy, to
around thirty pounds of high explosive. The landing is really
a euphemism for defusing this potential bomb. Because if
things go wrong through misjudgment, or bad weather, or a
combination of factors, all that dreadfully destructive kinetic
energy can mean very unpleasant consequences. The Harrier
pilot does not have to face these consequences. Using jet lift
from its vectored thrust, the Harrier can be flown in all
weather down to an approach speed of 100 knots or less compared with the conventional fighter's 200 knots approach.
The Harrier also approaches through a large "window,"
unlike the narrow limits of a conventional landing. The
conventional aircraft must be flown on a precise heading,
precise glide slope, and precise airspeed as the pilot hurtles
towards the mile-long strip of concrete, hoping all the way
that energy will be dissipated by the friction of his wheels, or
his tail parachute, before he reaches the end. The Harrier

pilot's transition to the hover above the runway is not critical in terms of speed, track, height or even wind direction. Any errors he may have made in any of these factors can be corrected at his leisure. After all, he is stopping *before* he lands. Three hundred pounds of fuel have been found sufficient for a transition from wingborne flight, and a prolonged hover over a landing area. A conventional jet pilot risks being "carpeted" if he attemps to land with that little fuel, since it leaves him nothing in reserve to make another circuit if he has misjudged his landing. This flexibility of landing has great attractions for the civil application of V/STOL, which will be discussed later in the book.

If the airplane is too heavy to take off vertically because its weight exceeds the engine thrust, then the wing is used to provide extra lift during a rolling takeoff. Because the aircraft is going to use the unique combination of wing lift plus vectored thrust from the engine, then only a very short run with dramatic acceleration is necessary. The takeoff run is started just like a conventional jet, but when the takeoff point is reached, the nozzles go down, and the aircraft leaps into the air. What then should the ground speed be? How far should the nozzles be put down in a short takeoff?

With any aircraft you can calculate how much lift you get from the wing at certain speeds. There is a fairly simple chart which says that if you are so many pounds over your VTO weight you will need so many knots for the wing to provide the necessary extra lift. As far as nozzle angle is concerned, clearly most lift is achieved if the engine thrust is pointed straight at the ground. However, if it is pointed vertically downwards, at the point of unstick, then the airplane leaps into the air, without enough thrust to maintain the speed at which it had been moving forward. The resistance of the air would slow the aircraft down, there would be a loss of wing lift, and down it would come again. The secret is, not to put them down all the way, but sufficiently backwards to give enough thrust to match the drag when the Harrier leaps into the air. Once again, there is a simple chart relating the drag of the aircraft to speed. In reality, a short takeoff is injecting the airplane halfway through the accelerating transition which follows a vertical takeoff.

During 1977 the airplane's accident record in the United States created a controversy. Up to September 1977, in the six and a half years of Marine Corps operations, twenty-six Harriers had crashed—that was about one fifth of their fleet—and fourteen of these crashes had occurred in the preceding nineteen months. Six of these Harriers were repairrable, but the human toll was ten pilots killed which, on the face of it, looked like a high accident rate. However, the statistics bear closer inspection.

Harrier losses in service have been at around the same per thousand flying hours as other equivalent aircraft operated in the ground attack role. In fact, the Harrier's loss rate is less that that of earlier conventional high power jet fighters like the Skyhawk, Phantom and Hunter, over the corresponding early years of their service life.

Of twenty-six U.S.M.C. accidents recorded early in the service life of the aircraft the Corps attribute twenty to pilot error. However, significantly, only eight of these involved pilot error in the unique V/STOL modes of operation. The remaining twelve crashes occurred due to pilot error in conventional flight when the Harrier was flying like any other fast jet. Four of the remaining crashes were blamed on material failure, and two on maintenance error.

The Marine Corps conceded that the sharp upward curve in their accident rate had been the result of a relaxation in their pilot standards. From 1974–1976 they had been selecting helicopter pilots for conversion to the Harrier after only one hundred hours or so of fixed wing jet training. This policy was aimed partly at preventing the Harrier squadrons becoming an elite or demanding very experienced pilots. But as the Marine Corps have now admitted, this policy was a mistake. The nucleus of Marine Corps Harrier pilots had been highly experienced conventional jet fighter pilots, many with experience over Vietnam, and the early accident rate was consequently very low. Lulled by this, the Corps decided to give a low priority to orders for the two-seat trainer version. However, with the intake of less experienced pilots into front line Harrier squadrons, the accidents began to mount sharply.

The training program was tightened. Harrier pilots now tend to come from the top 20 per cent of flight school graduates and increasing use is being made of the two-seat Harriers (TAV-8As) at U.S.M.C. Cherry Point.

In contrast to the Marine Corps, the Royal Air Force introduced the two-seat Harriers just over a year after the single seater entered service. Their loss rate in the first few years was relatively high and the accident rate curve shows the more normal trend, reducing as experience is gained in service.

The R.A.F. lost several Harriers in the early 70's due to engine failure after birdstrikes. At high speed and low level in the central Europe environment, birdstrike in the engine is a serious problem. But, although scores of birdstrikes in engine and airframe still occur each year, only eight aircraft have been lost in this way since 1969—and that figure includes all the air forces using the Harrier. This reduced vulnerability to birds is due principally to the introduction of the manual fuel control system which we'll look at later.

Using one accepted yardstick, the aircraft is near the top of the safety league when compared with all other comparable fighter/attack aircraft. For the factor to remember when considering the Harrier's accident rate is that these statistics are usually calculated on accidents per 10,000 flying hours.

The conventional takeoff and landing fighter or attack aircraft operates from a base well behind the battle zone and hence flies for a relatively long time, per attack or per takeoff and landing. Or the pilot can often spend a long time "loiter-ing" just behind the battle zone, in the air, awaiting the call to attack a target. The Harrier flies short-range sorties from rudimentary bases much closer to the battle zone. Or the Harrier pilot, flying from a base further to the rear, lands ver-tically at a forward site to await his call to an assigned target. He loiters on the ground.

Either way the Harrier clocks up far fewer flight hours per target hit, or per takeoff and landing than his colleague flying a conventional jet. Since history shows that accidents are more likely to occur in the attack and in the T.O. and L. phases of a mission, the Harrier suffers by comparison on a "per 10,000 hours" basis.

On the basis of losses per sortie or per takeoff and land-ing, the Harrier has one of the best safety records when set against all other comparable fighter/attack aircraft. What a blow to those who talk glibly of "the penalty you pay for V/STOL!"

If a pilot has jet experience, then the basic simplicity of the Harrier concept normally presents no problem. Experi-enced pilots are normally checked out on the two-seat Harri-er after five hours. New pilots, straight from Royal Air Force advanced flying and tactical warfare training are flying Harriers solo after six or seven hours. Of course, to operate it as a fighting weapons system, using the aircraft's navigation and attack system, is another matter.

Both Royal Air Force and U.S. Marine Corps Harriers started out with the Ferranti Fe 541 Inertial Navigation and Attack System (INAS), although the Marines have since opted for a much more basic system principally because of the "warm-up" period required on the ground by the Ferranti system, and also because of the technical problem of aligning an inertial system on board ships at sea. We will look at the Marine Corps' system later.

If we are talking about this highly sophisticated system

(Ferranti), it's worth making comparisons with the navigation and attack system of the Royal Air Force's previous ground-attack fighter, the Hawker Hunter. It's a bit like comparing the bow and arrow to the automatic rifle. Hunter pilots relied principally on stopwatches and a map on their knee. True, they did have a radio aid called DME (Distance Measuring Equipment) which was linked to beacons and was supposed to tell pilots where they were by measuring the distance between the beacons. But, it was unreliable, could often be as much as five miles out, and relied on continuous transmissions from the ground. Of course, in modern times, it's very doubtful that navigational systems which rely on ground transmissions would escape jamming, so the INAS was designed, from the outset, as a self-contained "on-board" system. All that its computer requires is to be told the longitude and latitude to a tenth of a minute of arc (or a hundred yards or so) of where the aircraft is sitting on the ground. From there on, the pilot is told continuously where he is, what height he is at, how fast he is going, how far to the target, what he should steer to get home, and so on.

The basis of the system is an inertial platform held level to a high degree of accuracy by gyroscopes and linked to a computer inside the aircraft. On the platform are three accelerometers which sense changes of velocity—one forwards and backwards, one left and right, the other up and down. This platform is continually doing simple maths based on the premise that speed attained is acceleration multiplied by time, and the distance covered is speed times time. So, the inertial platform is continuously feeding into the computer the aircraft's position in relation to the ground.

Another system called the Air Data Computer works out how the air is moving past the aircraft. Before the airplane takes off, there might be a sixty knot wind blowing, and the airspeed indicator in the aircraft will read 60. After takeoff on a particular heading, there will be a particular angle of drift, depending on which direction this wind is blowing towards it. The sensors of the Air Data Computer feed in the information that the sixty knot wind is blowing from the south and tending to push the aircraft in a northerly direction. By comparing the results from the inertial platform and the Air Data Computer, the navigation system automatically tells the pilot where he is. If there were no wind at all, then the air data would be exactly the same as the ground data.

The information from these computers is available to the pilot through his moving map and head-up displays. The moving map display is like a small television set on which you see a map. The area of the map is about ten miles in radius with the position of your aircraft at the center, and the map appears to move around behind the screen. The pilot can select any map he wishes, by slotting in a film cassette which covers an area about a thousand miles square. The film is projected on to the map screen, and the computer adjusts the map continuously to show the pilot his position.

Another presentation available is that the map can be orientated either north-south, or what is known as track-orientated, at the flick of a switch. Some pilots like to navigate with north at the top of the map at all times. Others like to swing it around so that it is linked with the direction of travel so what is ahead on the ground is at the top of the map. This is a facility that is greatly appreciated by the pilots.

The head-up display uses a cathode ray tube to superimpose symbolic and numerical data on the pilot's forward view through his windscreen. He can use it for control during vertical short takeoff and landing, general navigation, and air-to-ground attack. In fact, he can use it as a complete flight information panel without putting his eyes down into the cockpit at all. Most of the advantages of this are obvious, but one of them is of particular help in the Royal Air Force Harriers' ground attack role. They fly low—that's 250 feet or in wartime as low as they possibly can. In the Falklands campaign they were often down to around 20 feet above the undulating terrain. The reasons are very sensible. The enemy neither hears nor sees them coming, and even radar can be cheated "on the deck" by making use of obstructions like hills. The advantages of flying low increase the lower you fly. Clearly, at that level, the pilot does not want to look down at his instruments for fear of flying into the ground. With the HUD, vital information the pilot needs is projected in luminescent grey-green numbers on his windscreen, so that with his eyes focused on infinity he has a data display and is not faced with a bewildering range of information which he has to sift through. Depending on his task, he can select at the touch of a switch a variety of different displays which give him only the relevant instrument readings.

Another part of the nav/attack system denied to pilots of a previous aircraft generation, is the ability the Harrier pilot has to store information. In a Hunter ground attack mission, the pilot on his way to attack a bridge or a tank park, might well fly over an equally tempting target en route, that no one yet knows about. The Hunter pilot trying to steer a precise heading, and trying to count down on his stopwatch to the next landmark to change his heading, would see this target flash past him. He would be lucky to know precisely where he was and would scrawl a cross on his map as he pressed on to his main target, hoping to come back and find the "target of opportunity" later. The Harrier pilot has eight destination buttons through which he will have fed in the positions of his briefed target and turning points before takeoff. He also has a button marked "unplanned destination." As he passes over the new target he presses this button, and its position is accurately stored in the computer. He drops some weapons on the other target, then presses the "unplanned destination" button again, and the computer plus moving map will lead him back to the secondary target.

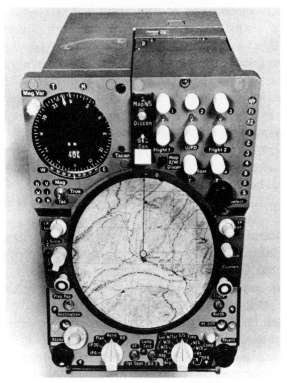

The navigation display component of the Ferranti INAS (Inertial Navigation and Attack System). White destination selection buttons are top right. The Target of Opportunity selection switch is center bottom.

Pilots are still trained, of course, in the traditional stop-watch and map methods of navigation. Some R. A. F. Harrier pilots in Germany who know the terrain over which they are flying extremely well, still prefer, generally speaking, to use this means rather than the INAS. That is perhaps a pessimistic view in that it presupposes that the land battle in any future European war would mean Harriers flying over their own terrain as opposed to Warsaw Pact country. Even those pilots concede the value of the INAS in telling them their accurate position if they were to be "bounced" on the way to a target and had to engage in air combat before pressing on to the target. Also, traditional methods are still vital back-up because the sophisticated system might fail for a variety of reasons, including battle damage. In that case, it has three reversionary modes where the pilot uses fewer and fewer facilities, the lowest being that it may simply be able to tell him how to get back home. If it cannot even do that, he had better have a map with him.

There is another reason for the traditional skills. Generally speaking, if the INAS does start to go wrong, it doesn't just go off a little—it fails. For example, if the system is monitored with occasional map-reading checks, and, for example, if a pilot has a shrewd idea that a bridge is five miles away and the computer says it's only three and a half, then it's almost certain that the computer is right. However, if the computer shows that it is 120 miles away, the pilot will have to fall back on his basic skills to press the mission home.

The overall navigation system also provides an accurate automatic attack system, because if the computer knows where the plane is and the pilot tells it where the target is, it can and does drop the bombs for him. The information fed into the computer before takeoff for the target might well have been a few hundred yards out. That is an acceptable navigational error, but quite unacceptable for weapons-aiming. Therefore, in automatic bombing, the computer must be updated almost at the last moment with a really accurate statement of where the target is. There is a cross in the head-up display which the pilot steers with his thumb. He turns the little knob until the cross is sitting right on top of the target. By doing this the computer knows where the target is and will release the bomb at the right moment.

This, of course, requires reasonable weather so that the pilot can physically see his target. Now, with the latest laser equipment being fitted to the Harrier, visual identification by the pilot is no longer necessary. For example, a soldier on the ground points a laser, at, say, a tank parked in some trees. The beam is reflected to the aircraft's own laser in the nose which tells the computer where the target is. Although it is feasible, of course, that the enemy could be using counter measures and pointing his own laser at an empty hole in the wood, lasers can be coded so that the pilot would hope to identify his own and ignore the enemy's. All these aids do not mean that the pilot of the Harrier has less to do than his predecessors. His workload is in fact greater, because systems like INAS have freed him to do more work, more effectively.

The Marine Corps bought the Harrier "off the shelf," which meant that apart from changing the insignia on the side, the altimeter and a few other small items, it was exactly the same as the R.A.F. aircraft, including the Ferranti INAS. There was a fierce internal struggle within the Marine Corps between those who disagreed about whether advantages of the system outweighed the twelve minutes "warm-up" which the inertial system required to align itself before takeoff. The Marines, of course, wanted the aircraft for close support of their troops during amphibious landings. The R.A.F., on the other hand, had a prime requirement for a single, low level, high speed attack. The U.S.M.C. war would be fought over short ranges from ten to forty miles and swift reaction times were a matter of life and death to the troops on the ground. When they called for air support, they wanted it as quickly as humanly possible. The Harrier had been chosen as the ideal aircraft for that job. During the warm-up time of the INAS, it was argued, the Marines on the ground could have been over-run. Besides, their attacks would be mainly on targets marked visually with flares or smoke shells. They thought then that the Ferranti system was a splendid piece of equipment, but

A test Harrier in 1970 flying with 8,000 lb. of warload. The Harrier is the fifth production R. A. F. aircraft XV742 temporarily wearing U. S. M. C. insignia for that year's Farnborough Show.

perhaps just too sophisticated for their purposes. A sledgehammer to crack a nut? Out it came.

The Marines decided to revert to the system which most of their attack aircraft had been using in Vietnam. It was in fact the fixed depression sight, which had been in the R. A. F. aircraft as a secondary system to the Ferranti equipment. The pilot has to pre-set the "pipper" or weapons aiming symbol on the head-up display. He then has to roll into his attack at a precise dive angle and airspeed and release the bombs at a precise altitude. If any of these three factors are not exactly as predetermined, then the bombs will not strike the target the pilot is looking at through his pipper. Experienced dive-bombers can develop almost a second sense which enables them to make adjustments to compensate, during the attack. However, this is the work for which Marine pilots train. Despite the comparative crudeness of the attack system, they consider their pilots efficient enough to give the really close-in support the ground troops demand. In fact, the system is an improvement over the aircraft like the Skyhawk, in that it is roll-stabilized. In the Skyhawk, when a pilot rolls in at bank angles up to 110 degrees, the pipper moves across with the bank. So, as the wings are rolled level again on the final run the weapons-aiming symbol is swinging like a pendulum and requires constant adjustments. In the Harrier, with roll-stabilization, the pipper always remains in the vertical on the head-up display close to where the target is. It makes bombing that much easier.

The U.S.M.C. has now introduced an attack system based on a continuously computed impact point. It is a computer aboard the aircraft which takes the airspeed from the air data computer, the barometric altitude from the altimeter and the dive angle from the gyroscope. Knowing the characteristic of the weapon involved it calculates an impact point. Whenever the pilot pushes the "pickle" (release button), the bomb will strike wherever the pipper is pointing. This is very different from the fixed depression sight which requires the pilot to pass through a "window" in the sky when he "pickles" the bombs. For the advanced Harrier, the AV-8B, the angle rate bombing system will depend on a laser or television signal locking on to the target with computers and calculating weapons release automatically.

Reconnaissance is another Harrier role, and for this it is fitted with a recce pod, under the center fuselage. It has five cameras, which give it a sweep of coverage from one horizon to the other. One camera on either side points slightly left and right; another pair points well to the left and right; and another points straight down. If the button is pressed selecting all cameras on, each single exposure of film has printed on it automatically the latitude and longitude of the airplane at that precise moment, its heading, and its speed and height. All from the INAS. Back on the ground, this system has transformed photographic interpretation.

Chapter 3

Harrier at War

It was mid-afternoon on May 1, 1982. Two grey-coloured Sea Harrier fighters flew a figure-of-eight pattern high above the British task force off the Falkland Islands. On the islands, the Argentine garrison were bracing themselves for the British landings. On the ships of the fleet, they stood at battle stations, radars probing towards the west for enemy attack aircraft. Lieutenant Steve Thomas, Fleet Air Arm, and Flight Lieutenant Paul Barton of the Royal Air Force were on combat air patrol. They scanned the small radar screens in their cockpits. Suddenly, the blips of two Mirage fighters of the Argentine Air Force appeared. On the windscreen in front of Steve Thomas, the luminescent green symbols of the weapons-aiming computer and navigation system gave him steering commands to intercept the targets. He followed the symbols on the screen, hauling the Harrier into a turn at full power. His air speed indicator showed 550 knots. Now he and wingman Barton had maneuvred into a firing position. Their eyes flicked constantly to their rear view mirrors and one or the other craned his head swiftly back and round, to detect any other enemy aircraft. Two very fast-moving smoke trails streaked towards the Harriers. Steve ducked instinctively as air-to-air missiles flashed over his cockpit canopy. They had drawn the enemy's fire. Inside Paul Barton's helmet there was a growl which told him he had locked on to the target. He pressed the lock button, released the safety catch, and fired. The Sidewinder heat-seeking missile leapt from its pylon rails under the wing, there was a flash and it hurtled towards the Mirage. Seconds later the Mirage exploded in a brilliant flash and a ball of flame. The other dived for the cloud layer below, pursued by a Sidewinder from Steve Thomas which accelerated towards the glowing tailpipe. It plunged into the cloud, and they couldn't confirm that the missile had struck.

The Harrier had gone to war. The revolutionary little jump jet had claimed its first ever "kill" in combat. And during the rest of the Falklands conflict it was to go on to destroy between 20–30 fast jets of the Argentine Air Force and Navy in air combat. The total estimated number of Argentine aircraft losses, including helicopters and transports and aircraft destroyed on the ground, was 117. Nine Harriers were lost, all due to either accident or enemy ground fire. Not one was downed by an Argentine fighter. The subsonic British jet, operating like its supersonic Mirage adversaries, at near the limit of its fuel range, took on and crushed an enemy of overwhelming numerical superiority. Without the Harrier and its unique vertical and short take-off and landing capability, the British government would have been faced with little alternative but to concede humiliating concession of the Argentinian seizure of the Falkland Islands in the early part of 1982. For, a government decision in the late 60's phased out large strike carriers and their conventional fixed-wing air power, and until a decision was made to adapt the Harrier to a naval role, the Fleet Air Arm had been declining towards a helicopter-only force. To have sent a task force without fixed wing air cover 8,000 miles into the South Atlantic against heavily defended islands and a large modern air force would have been inconceivable both politically and militarily. The eyes of the military throughout the world were concentrated on the combat performance of the Harrier. The Harrier's fighting ability, reliability, and almost infinite flexibility astonished those outsiders. But to the men who flew it, knew it, and loved it, the Falklands experience was simply an affirmation of their faith.

That same day, as dusk fell, the Harriers added to their tally. Guided by Lieutenant Bob Holmes, the fighter controller on board the carrier *Invincible,* Lieutenant Alan Curtis and Lieutenant Commander Mike Broadwater were guided by ship's radar on to three Canberra jet bombers. The Argentines had approached the fleet at high level, then dived rapidly to just above the waves to make their attack on the fleet. The ship lost radar contact 100 miles out and the Harriers used their own radar to make a classic interception. Under very low cloud, Alan Curtis guided the pair into a firing position behind the Canberras. Both Harriers fired Sidewinders and watched them rush towards the enemy.

The lead bomber exploded and the wreckage fell into the waves. Mike Broadwater's target had already turned back towards the mainland and, although it was not downed immediately, it was reported to have crashed into the sea as it limped homewards. A Sea Harrier from the other carrier, *Hermes,* had also destroyed a Mirage. As the task force ploughed through the heavy seas, on both carriers there was a celebration below decks. Above, on the flight deck, pilots sat strapped in their cockpits waiting to scramble to intercept any night attackers. The instruments glowed faintly on the faces under the helmets. They sat in their immersion flying suits, with the pins removed from the right-hand side of the cockpit to make the ejection seat "live." Outside the aeroplane the flight deck crews struggled against the buffeting wind and the

freezing spray. Ahead of the pilots was the curve of the
Ski-Jump take-off ramp. And beyond that was the total
blackness of the ocean at night.

The Sea Harrier pilots knew before they fired a shot in
anger that they had a dog-fighting aircraft of unique agility, a
jet without great inherent turning ability in its wing design,
but one which could use its swivelling nozzles to out-fight any
adversary it had ever tackled in air combat exercises. And the
British aircrew had had a tremendous boost to their morale not
long before they embarked for the Falklands. In exercises in
Sardinia they had taken on, and beaten every time, the
American F5 fighters, and the F15 Eagle, one of the U.S.A.F.'s
principal air superiority fighters. They had proved it in war
games. Now, when ships were burning below them and men
were dying, they would prove it again in the heat of battle.

A Sea Harrier take-off from the carriers was preceded by
intense activity in the cockpit as flight deck officers tried to
keep up the momentum of the deck cycle of re-arming,
re-fuelling and launch. Four minutes before the launch, the
pilot climbed into his cockpit and started the vital pre-launch
checks. Then the engine started—fuel boost pumps on, start
selected, master pressed, HP fuel cock on. The instruments
showed that the jet pipe temperature was rising, the engine
was "burning." It took two minutes for the inertial navigation
system to align and establish the aircraft's position in its
computer. The aircraft was unlashed from its deck restraints
and the engine was slammed to half power to check that
acceleration time was within the permitted 3 to 4.5 seconds.
The pilot showed the flat of his hand on the canopy to tell the
flight deck officer that he accepted the launch. The FDO's
handdropped and the pilot slammed the throttle forward. Ten
tons of Pegasus engine thrust pushed him back into his seat as
the Harrier accelerated down the deck. In less than three
seconds his speed was 90 knots and he was off the edge of the
curving ramp, Immediately he was clear of the ramp he rotated

his engine nozzles down to 35 degrees and when the aircraft reached the end of its curving trajectory from the ramp he gently eased the nozzles until they were pointing straight backwards. He retracted landing gear and flaps and the air speed indicator showed that the tremendous thrust-to-weight ratio of this compact aircraft was accelerating him through 400 knots. He held the aircraft down to 200 feet until he got 500 knots airspeed, then pulled back on the stick and the Harrier drove straight up through the cloud. He had to roll it on to its back to slow down the rate of ascent as he was called by the fighter controller from the carrier and given a "vector." Then he set off to intercept the enemy.

On May 24, Lieutenant David Smith, 27, made his first "kill," flying as wingman with his "boss" Lieutenant-Commander Andy Auld of 800 Squadron on combat air patrol north of Pebble Island. H.M.S. *Broadsword,* which was on radar picket duty, had picked up a contact and they were told to intercept. They were vectored to 260 degrees, diving down to the surface at high speed. Lieutenant Smith tucked in behind the "boss" and as they passed through 550 knots in the dive, they were down to just 150 feet above the waves. They made a hard turn towards the enemy and Lieutenant-Commander Auld called out the single word "visual." There they were— four Mirages, very low and very fast. The Harrier leader pulled his nose up and rolled in behind the enemy formation, firing both his Sidewinders in quick succession. Both hit and two Mirages exploded almost simultaneously in violent fireballs. The second pair broke hard right and Smith locked on to one of them. The Mirage jettisoned his underwing fuel tanks and his bombs in a desperate attempt to improve his maneuvrability. But he was already doomed. The Sidewinder cut across the corner of his escape route and shot up his tail pipe. There was a tremendous flash and another fireball as the aircraft broke into pieces and hit the ground. In less than five seconds the pair had destroyed three enemy aircraft. They pursued the

Kestrels of the Tripartite Squadron in formation.

Indian Navy Sea Harriers of 300 (White Tiger) Squadron.

Royal Navy Sea Harriers of 801 Squadron.

Royal Navy Sea Harriers of 899 Squadron with twin Sidewinders mounted on outer pylons of nearest aircraft.

lone survivor as he raced west, but he stayed just out of missile range and, low on fuel, they had to break off. But they learned later that he had run out of fuel and had been forced to ditch.

On June 8, the day the *Sir Galahad* was hit, Lieutenant Smith was patrolling at 10,000 feet with Flight-Lieutenant Dave Morgan. Below them smoke poured from the burning ships at Bluff Cove, and the entire after section of the *Sir Galahad* was glowing red with the heat. The pilots were itching to have a go at the enemy. Dusk was falling when they spotted some Mirages attacking landing craft approaching from the direction of Goose Green. David Morgan rolled his Harrier upside down and, pulling his stick back hard, he dived for the surface, with Smith following him, trying hard to keep contact with the grey jet in the gathering gloom. His airspeed was around 600 knots when, about half a mile ahead, he saw two bright flashes from Morgan's Harrier. He watched the smoke trails from the Sidewinders as they pursued the Mirages. Again, the now familiar fireballs as the warheads exploded inside the fiery jetpipes to which their infra-red sensors had inexorably drawn them.

Morgan, with the fierce aggression of the true fighter pilot, was now attacking the other two Mirages with cannon fire from the Aden guns slung under his fuselage. He saw his wingman maneuvring behind him and broke out of the fight to give him a clear sight with his missiles. Smith heard the acquisition growl in his ears and released a Sidewinder. The range was perhaps two and a half miles and as he watched the smoke trail, it seemed to flame out just short of the target. Then a blinding flash pierced the gloom. A fraction of a second later, the Mirage impacted the ground.

The victorious pair were perilously low on fuel. They returned to the carrier at high level to save fuel on the long flight back, then, tense after the exhilaration of the combat, they were faced with the extremely demanding task of one of their first night vertical landings on the heaving deck of the carrier.

Once the ground forces were established ashore, a 300 yard long metal matting runway was laid by Royal Engineers across an area of grass and peat with a slight upward incline—this had the effect of giving the Harriers a modest "Ski Jump Effect" on take-off. Flexible aviation fuel bags were moored in a line along the shore and fuel was pumped from there to the strip. Ammunition, rockets and bombs were stock-piled and the area was protected by Rapier anti-aircraft missile batteries. It had become a forward operating base— part of the classic Harrier operating scenario.

What it meant was that Sea Harriers on Combat Air Patrol from the carriers could engage the enemy on full combat power for vital extra minutes, then land at the San Carlos FOB, instead of having to conserve fuel for a return to the carrier for re-fuelling and re-arming. Harriers on ground attack sorties were also able to spend longer over the islands. The aircraft also used the assault ships *Fearless* and *Intrepid,* close to San Carlos, as floating FOBs. There is no doubt in the minds of the pilots that these facilities played an important role in the air battles. On one day alone, the San Carlos FOB handled 19 Harrier and Sea Harrier movements.

The Harriers flew a total of 1650 sorties during a seven week period and only one per cent of planned missions could not be flown because of unserviceability. It is a truly remarkable record for a sophisticated modern combat aircraft, and much of the reliability can be attributed to the magnificent Rolls Royce Pegasus engine—despite the harsh treatment these engines were receiving in combat there was only one engine change necessary. The intense anti-aircraft fire around the heavily defended ground targets meant considerable battle damage to the airframe, but the Harriers proved they could take a great deal of punishment and still keep flying. Usually they were repaired and in the air within hours of sustaining the damage. The professionalism and commitment of the engineering and maintenance back-up was superb—and often innovative and ingenious. The relative humidity remained at 100 per cent for days at a time which meant that everything was dripping wet—including the electronics in the aircraft systems. Many aircraft had to be left on deck for days at a time. It was common for "black boxes" which were not functioning to be removed and put in a galley oven to dry. Plugs and sockets were dismantled and in some cases sealed with aerosol plastic skin borrowed from the sick bay. Household "clingfilm" was used with great success to cover cockpit instruments and control panels. And common bathroom sealant was used to plug joints to help prevent moisture seeping through.

The task force sailed for the South Atlantic in early April. Only a few people in Britain have ever been aware of a dramatic wrangle which could have turned the tide of the air battles against the British task force. The argument—over the type of air-to-air missile to be fitted to the R.A.F. and Royal Navy Harriers—was settled just before the fleet sailed, by an eleventh hour live firing test in the sky over the Welsh coast.

The drama centered on which variant of the Sidewinder AIM9 infra-red missile should be taken. The Royal Air Force, whose primary role in the Falklands was to be ground attack, not air-to-air combat, were pressing for the entire air group to take the tried and tested AIM9G. It is an excellent missile, combat proven in Vietnam and by the Israeli Air Force, but it has the limitation that it is not effective if fired head-on at an enemy aircraft. The AIM9L, however, can detect temperature wavelengths which are very cool so is capable of sensing heat emissions from the head-on sector. The problem is that it can also be attracted by a hot reflection from the ground—if the combat is at low level—or by the sun's reflection from a cloud. The Royal Air Force had been having some difficulties integrating the AIM9L into their Phantom fighters, so they were concerned that it wouldn't work properly on the Sea Harrier either.

A week before the task force sailed, a British Aerospace Sea Harrier test pilot, Taylor Scott, learned from the Directorate of Naval Air Warfare in the Ministry of Defence that the R.A.F. were pressing the Navy on the choice of missile. Scott, a 35-year-old-civilian, was a former Navy pilot. He was horrified by what he had been told. He was convinced it was a decision which could have the most serious effect on the ability of the outnumbered Fleet Air Arm to win the air combat against the Argentinian Mirage fighters. And he was in the best position to know.

He had been flying Royal Navy jets since he was 18, and had begun a close association with British Aerospace in June 1977, when he was seconded from the Navy to work on the weapons system development of the Sea Harrier at Dunsfold. John Farley, who was then still Chief Test Pilot, recognized his outstanding flying abilities and the company offered him a job as a test pilot on the Sea Harrier program. But he kept his rank of Lieutenant-Commander and his close links with former Fleet Air Arm colleagues by transferring to the reserve. It was this unusual position of "one foot in each camp" which led to a civilian playing such a decisive role in the Sidewinder affair, and later, too, in the remarkable formation of a new squadron for the conflict.

Scott had been test-flying and helping develop—with Smiths Industries, British Aerospace and Ministry engineers—a means of solving the deficiencies in the AIM9L. They had come up with answers, still highly classified, which convinced them that they could guarantee the missile's performance with the Sea Harrier. The difficulty was, that by the time Scott and his colleagues learned of the R.A.F.'s insistence on the AIM9G, time was running out. The only way to reverse the situation was to convince the Director of Naval Air Warfare that they were right and the R.A.F. were wrong.

Scott cancelled a test flight from Dunsfold Aerodrome on Wednesday, April 7, and drove to London. There he met a friend, Lieutenant-Commander Peter Walwyn, who, along with another Navy engineer, Lieutenant-Commander Peter Ling, had been working with him on the Sidewinder development program. They went in to see Commander Fred De Labilliere, the fixed wing adviser to the Director of Naval Air Warfare. It was a tense and occasionally heated meeting, but De Labilliere was convinced to the extent that he ordered them swiftly to write a test firing program. They were to be given six AIM9Ls to fire on the range at Aberporth on the Welsh coast that Saturday.

The other two pilots who flew the crucial test flight in Wales were Lieutenant-Commander David Poole, then attached to the government test establishment at Boscombe Down, and a Royal Australian Navy exchange pilot, David Ramsey. Tracked by radar, the six missiles were fired. Scott and the others flew their aircraft under extreme conditions, from as low as 100 feet all the way up to 35,000 feet. All the launches were head-on. One missile was faulty. The others scored direct hits or misses so near they registered as "kills." Back in London, R.A.F. and Royal Navy commanders at the highest level waited for the results to be phoned from Aberporth. On Sunday, the decision was announced. The R.A.F. and Royal Navy's Harriers would be armed with the AIM9L.

In the event, the Argentinian pilots concentrated on attacking the task force ships. There was none of the high altitude dog-fighting with the tight-turning Mirages, which the British pilots had anticipated. Most engagements took place at low level—50 to 500 feet—and at speeds in excess of 550 knots, where the Harrier's high combat agility and high thrust, low fuel consumption engine scored every time. And most of the Sidewinder firings by the Harriers were from the rear quarter, where the missiles rushed up the enemy tailpipes and literally blew the aircraft apart. We view this now with the benefit of hindsight. But in the anticipated combat scenario, the choice of missiles could have been crucial to the control of the air.

The three existing Sea Harrier squadrons had been divided in April between the two task force carriers *Hermes* and *Invincible*. *Hermes* later also embarked R.A.F. Harriers. Royal Navy squadrons 800 and 801 went south, along with their headquarters and training unit, 899 Squadron. This meant that the entire Fleet Air Arm fighter strength had sailed for the South Atlantic. At any given time, due to losses, there were never more than 32 Harriers aboard the two carriers, for both interception and ground attack and support missions. It was a slender air force to send 8,000 miles into some of the most hostile weather in the world, against land-based, numerically superior air strength. As the task force sailed towards the Falklands there were, inevitably, some pessimistic predictions about aircraft losses. Harrier reinforcements were an immediate priority, and the Royal Naval Air Station at Yeovilton in Somerset was to be the base for an astonishing exercise which produced a new eight aircraft Sea Harrier squadron in an unprecedented three-week period. The squadron was designated 809.

Taylor Scott was given leave by British Aerospace to help lead the training team. The others were Lieutenant-Commander Jock Gunning, David Ramsey, the Australian Navy pilot who had flown the Sidewinder test, and a United States Marine Corps pilot, Captain Willie McAtee. The 12 squadron pilots were rounded up from R.A.F. squadrons in the UK and Germany and several were even recalled from exchange tours in America and Australia. All had had some experience in Harriers, but some—the so-called "first tourists"—had only a few hours. Most had little or no knowledge of the Sea Harrier weapons system, and some had never even seen a radar screen in a cockpit before. The task for Scott and the rest of the training team was truly daunting.

The work-up started at Yeovilton on April 17. They had

*Lining up at Stanley Airport for Falklands sortie take-off —
Royal Air Force GR3 Harrier with laser nose, twin Aden
gun pods on the center line pylons and Sidewinder
air-to-air missiles on outer, pylons.*

*Re-arming Sea Harriers with Sidewinders on board H.M.S.
Hermes during the air battles of the Falklands campaign.*

R.A.F. GR3 Harrier performs a rolling vertical landing on a German road during field deployment exercise.

three aircraft—a two-seat TMK8N Hunter trainer with the full Sea Harrier weapons system, and two Sea Harriers, one without radar and the other without either radar or navigation system. Not the most promising basic equipment, as the Harriers were very basic, simply flying machines. They had three major jobs: to teach the new squadron's pilots how to use the radar, how to "toss" bombs and air combat maneuvring—dog-fighting techniques.

They flew seven days a week, starting with a briefing session at 7.30 a.m. and often not ending until 10 p.m. It was still thought then that the Argentine Air Force would attack at night, so a good knowledge of radar was needed. They worked on tactics to combat the Mirage at night both at high and low altitudes. Using the Hunter with the Sea Harrier weapons system, the training team worked through the pilots, teaching intercept techniques which involved the Head Up Display (see chapter 2) for weapons aiming and release, in conjunction with the radar.

The automation in the system was such, that provided they got radar lock on to their target, the steering information in the HUD on the windscreen would lead them to an intercept without too much difficulty. But there's a tremendous skill involved, for the pilot must learn to fly the aircraft accurately, while looking down at the radar and adjusting with his fingers the elevation of the radar scan which is trying to track the enemy. The elevation is crucial, because if the enemy is high and you're looking low, you'll miss him. The secret, the new pilots learned, was to fly first and sort out the weapons system second. As experience is gained, more time can be devoted to the radar. What they were being taught was a system which over-rode much of the need for great mental agility—a system designed by British Aerospace to provide a simple steering command for the pilot to follow. This training was very much oriented to offensive tactics. It advanced from pre-planned flights against another aircraft, on to air combat where the target would be violently evading and making life as difficult as possible. Night and day, they would fly against two, three or four "enemy" aircraft and as often as possible against dissimilar types, like the Phantom.

Taylor Scott recalled: "News of the first losses started to come in from the Falklands. The Harrier community is a small one, and we all knew the chaps who had been killed. It's desperately saddening, but in a strange way it was almost a morale builder, because we hadn't lost anyone in air combat with the Argentines. If that had been happening, we'd really have had to tighten down."

They had also been working on their toss-bombing technique, which is a method of delivering bombs on a target without having to overfly it or dive-bomb it—techniques which expose the aircraft to ground fire and the possibility of being struck by fragments from their own bombs. The technique uses the Sea Harrier radar to give information which will steer the aircraft to the target. About two miles from the target, the Head Up Display will give the command to the pilot to pull up from his low level approach. As he pulls up, the bombs are automatically released. He rolls out and escapes in the opposite direction while the bombs carry on in their trajectory for around 30 seconds before striking the target. It was a method used for the first Harrier attack on Stanley airfield, with one group of Harriers toss-bombing, and another sweeping across the airfield seconds later from another direction, with retard-fused bombs, as the defenders were still recovering from the first attack.

The new squadron was now ready to go to war. Their aircraft had been pulled together from a variety of sources—the existing aircraft at Yeovilton, from Boscombe Down and five from the war reserve. They flew off to Ascension Island, refuelling several times during the nine-hour flight, before loading on to the *Atlantic Conveyor* for the journey to their aircraft carriers off the Falklands. Left behind was a very frustrated Taylor Scott.

Throughout the intense training period of 809 Squadron, he had been trying to speed up his call-up from the reserve, to active service. He could not go as a civilian—that would have made him a mercenary. The intention had been that he would go as the squadron's air warfare instructor but he waved the squadron goodbye, still awaiting his call-up. It did not come until June 1, and in the interim he carried on training another batch of potential Falklands Sea Harrier pilots. He eventually joined the Harrier force in the South Atlantic after the surrender.

The Royal Air Force Harriers which flew from the carrier *Hermes* were fitted with Sidewinder missiles too, but only for their own defense if they had to fight Argentine aircraft during their missions—ground attack in support of the British troops. They did not have the radar intercept ability of the Sea Harriers, but they were trained specifically for the role they played in the Falklands—extremely low level, following the contours of the ground at high speed and attacking their targets on the first pass. It was a role they practised every day in Britain and in Europe where, in a future war, they would hit Warsaw Pact armour at "choke points" on the North German Plain. They were not able to use their extremely accurate laser-bombing technique until near the end of the conflict but they played a major role in supporting the ground forces.

Squadron-Leader Bob Iveson, a flight commander in No. 1 Squadron R.A.F., was shot down on May 27 during his second sortie of the day. His mission had been ground attack in support of the 2nd Battalion Parachute Regiment as they attacked the heavily defended Goose Green airfield. He took off from *Hermes* with his wingman, briefed to hit several targets, including a large field gun and enemy troop positions. At around 600 miles an hour and fifty feet above the ground, a gun is a tiny target. There was no accurate target marking from the ground forces and Iveson swept over the area on his first pass without detecting it. Hugging the ground, he turned for another pass and saw his secondary target, the Argentine troop positions. He dropped his cluster bombs and they each opened up to release 147 bomblets which spread in a deadly exploding pattern along the positions. Bob Iveson was convinced the Paras were in serious trouble so he decided to make another attack. He came in very low and very fast, sending a long burst of cannon fire right along the line of the trenches. He pulled up to reverse his flight path for another attack and had descended again to a hundred feet when he was hit. He knew they were heavy calibre shells because he felt two heavy thumps one after the other.

Almost immediately, the fire warning light came on and fumes seeped into the cockpit. The flying controls froze completely—a quick look at the instruments revealed that hydraulic pressure was dropping at an alarming rate. He punched the fire extinguisher system and a glance in his rear view mirror revealed flames licking along the top of the fuselage. Smoke started to pour into the cockpit, then the controls went slack and the Harrier nosed into a dive. He pulled the nozzle lever and directed the thrust of the engine downwards. The nose picked up but at the same time, flames started to lick into the cockpit itself. The irony was that the marvellous Pegasus engine was still running sweetly, but it was clearly time to get out. He pulled the ejection handle between his legs, the explosive charges in the canopy shattered a hole and a fraction of a second later he was hurtled from the airplane by his rocket ejection seat. He passed out for a few seconds and when he came round he was flying horizontally through the air—straight for the fireball of his burning aircraft.

Then, the main parachute opened and he floated clear of that danger. It only seemed around ten seconds before he was on the ground. His eyes were blurred from the force of the ejection and as he freed himself from his 'chute, he thought he saw a line of dots coming down a hillside. They could have been sheep, but equally, as he peered through his soft focus, they could have been enemy troops looking for him. He ran off in the opposite direction and eventually found a deserted farmhouse.

Bob Iveson knew the Argentinians were looking for him. That night a helicopter with a large searchlight came clattering towards his hiding place. It stopped, hovering over one spot—possibly the remains of the Harrier. Iveson thought that capture wasn't far away, as the helicopter advanced towards his refuge, but at that moment a night attack on Goose Green was launched and the helicopter broke away. He spent the following two days, either hiding in the heather or in the farmhouse, huddled at night against the freezing cold, chewing his emergency rations. He was picked up on May 29 by a Royal Marine helicopter pilot who had been courageously searching for him. The next day he was ferried back to *Hermes* on a Sea King helicopter.

In the same area, at that time, another Sea King was plucking from the water, Bob Iveson's good friend squadron-Leader Jerry Pook who ejected from his battle-damaged Harrier after heavy fuel loss. In a touching display of the comradeship which binds such men together, Pook had flown a solo sortie, on the day his friend was shot down, vainly searching for signals from the personal radio Iveson carried in his lifejacket.

For over 20 years, the Harrier has been the most misunderstood military aircraft in the world. The Falklands conflict, unfortunately, did little to change many of the misconceptions about its capabilities.

Proponents of the aircraft had been saying for years that what was necessary to show the world its worth, was a sharp, short war—without, of course, too many casualties. The Falklands provided the ideal opportunity for this most public of demonstrations, and the Harrier performed brilliantly in combat—beyond even the expectations of its most fervent supporters.

Its reliability was extraordinary; in air combat, despite its sub-sonic performance, its thrust-to-weight ratio gave it enormous acceleration in the low level pursuits of Argentinian aircraft; and almost as soon as the troops were ashore the Harriers were operating in support from their short metal runways.

Without the Harrier, there would have been no task force. In Britain's fighting inventory, no other aircraft—all dependent upon runways within range of the battleground— were even remotely suitable.

However, the vested interest in long airfield runways and large aircraft carriers, for big, heavy supersonic jets, is strong and firmly entrenched. As soon as the euphoria over the Harrier's Falklands performance had subsided, the arguments against the aircraft—discussed earlier in this book—were raised again.

And others were added: the Falklands was a unique situation which other countries were never likely to be faced with; even for the British it was a complete "one-off," and so on.

The Falklands conflict proved that all the technical claims made for the Harrier were correct. It seems unlikely that they will be enough to persuade the air forces of the world to discard their prejudices.

Chapter 4

The Leap Beyond
the Rivals

It was a bold decision in 1958 for Hawker to carry on with the airframe development using their own cash. Three-quarters of the engine funding had been provided for the engine makers by the American Mutual Weapons Development Program in Paris, but the airframe continued to be funded privately until June 1960—only a few months before the P1127 first hovered. The Ministry of Aviation issued a contract for two prototypes and four more development aircraft. Although it was not much, it was the first concrete encouragement from the U. K. establishment. It also reflected the prevailing opinion that the future of vertical takeoff and landing military aircraft still lay in the multi-engine concept as demonstrated by the Rolls Royce-powered Short SC1. Still, it meant that the P1127 was no longer private venture development, and it gave the design team an added incentive to solve the problems which were beginning to appear.

The basic conflict inherent in any vertical takeoff and landing aircraft is between thrust and weight. The thrust pushed out by the engine must exceed the overall weight of the airplane, or it will remain very firmly on the ground. With the P1127 the issue was complicated by the relatively low thrust—11,500 pounds—which the first Pegasus produced. This meant the designers were faced with producing an airframe much lighter in relation to its size than anything they had previously attempted. The Hunter, a very conventional, high performance, subsonic swept wing fighter had a structure which accounted for something like a third of its weight at takeoff. If the 1127 airframe had been taken to that degree of structural ruggedness, weighing a third of its takeoff weight, it would have had no spare capacity to carry any military payload. Their target with this new aircraft was a structure-weight ratio of a quarter or less than the weight, which was unheard of in a high G fighter airframe at that time. Still they did it.

Simplicity was the guiding principle. The fuselage was short, blunt and rather fat in relation to its length. The length meant less weight of metal, and they did not mind the bluntness of the fuselage either, because in aerodynamic terms, they were only aiming for high subsonic speeds, not minimum drag for supersonic flight performance. The same aerodynamic parameters applied to the wing which also had to be capable of carrying a lot of fuel. The first wing planform shape was a forty-five degrees delta shape with an unswept trailing edge. The tail unit was as small as they could make it consistent with the requirements of pilot control in flight.

It was hardly surprising, considering the constraints of weight and the obligation to wrap it around this large engine, that the first prototype looked very strange when it was wheeled out. The funny bicycle-type undercarriage with strange outriggers on the wings. This was the configuration that Sir Sydney Camm had had such dark forebodings about, but really there was not much else they could do with it. A conventional undercarriage with a nosewheel and main wheels on the wings was out because it was impossible to retract the main wheels sideways into the wings. The alternative of retracting them backwards into large "blisters" behind the wing trailing edge would have caused excessive drag and interfered with flaps and aileron function. No matter how Sir Sydney fumed, it seemed he was stuck with it.

Chief Test Pilot Bill Bedford and his colleague Hugh Merewether were brought in on the fringe of the design prob-

Hugh Merewether, Chief Test Pilot at Dunsfold from 1967–70. He made a major contribution to the flight development of the Harrier.

lems on the ill-fated P1121 project, and throughout that period, they continued development flying on the various marks of the highly successful Hunter. Bedford took a professional interest in the general concept of vertical takeoff and landing, and cast a quizzical eye over reports on things like the Flying Bedstead and Short SC1. However, in common with most other professional pilots at that time, he found it difficult to relate these projects to a practical civil or military application. They seemed either crude or excessively complicated to control and the general impression was that fuel consumption would be impractical.

On his visits to the drawing office at Kingston, from the test flying base at Dunsfold, Bill Bedford saw unusual configuration sketches on drawing boards. But work at that time was still progressing on the P1121, and besides, one was always seeing new ideas being sketched out. Design offices live or die by their creativity, but only a small percentage of these ideas are ever transformed into flying machines. Although he was to play a major part in the aircraft's development, Bedford was not an instant convert, even when the company gave it their official sanction. It did not take long, though, before he was drawn into the program and was involved in the run-up to the first flight.

Bedford, like the others at Hawker, was imbued with the Camm dictum of "keep it simple." He applied this vigorously to his thoughts on how the new aircraft was to be controlled. It had already been decided to control it in the hover by using the system of puffers at nose, wing tips and tail. They started out trying to use low pressure fan air from the engine because it had much less energy and it was less erosive when poured at the ground. It also bled less of the vital thrust of the engine. But, the physical size of the ducting leading around the airframe became more and more cumbersome, so they had to take a deep breath and go for high pressure air. A deep breath, because it meant the ducting around the aircraft would now be hot, and the understandable fear was that if flammable fluids dropped on it there would be an explosion. In fact, they tried long and hard, in the laboratory, to get an explosion, and failed. Their decision to go for high pressure air still posed problems of thermal insulation for the piping, but the problem of loss of engine thrust was a much bigger headache.

In the present aircraft, the reaction control puffers work on a demand system. They remain closed unless the pilot's movement of stick or rudder bar opens them to send out a jet of air which adjusts the aircraft's position. This means that every available pound of pressure from the engine is working to support the aircraft above the ground. In the early flights of the prototypes, the system was planned to be much less sophisticated. The valves were to be partially open at all times, bleeding vitally needed thrust from an engine which was struggling to achieve vertical takeoff. It would cane the engine, for as well as reducing its already limited thrust, it would make the turbine temperature soar. These were problems which lay in the future for Bill Bedford and his test flight colleagues. They were already aware before the aircraft ever left the ground that to make it fail-safe they would have to ensure that it could be flown manually.

Autostabilization was all very well, they reasoned, but they did not want to produce an aircraft which was uncontrollable without it. The Ministry of Supply had been reluctant in the first place to give any funding to Hawker because of their skepticism at the planemakers' insistence that such aircraft could be controlled in the hover without full autostabilization. Hawker then pulled a really impudent stroke. They fed into a simulator all the skills which a human being requires to ride and control a bicycle. According to the simulator, it was quite impossible for any human being to ride a bicycle unless the bike was equipped with autostabilization!

The search for the best control system to fly the P1127

The 1/10th scale powered model of the P1127 on which all the early work on hovering in ground effect was done at Hawker's Kingston factory during 1959–60.

brought them once again to the American connection—the strong thread which continued to run throughout the aircraft's development. Early in 1960, Ralph Hooper went to the United States and met John Stack, the director of NASA at Langley Field, who was later to die tragically in a riding accident. Hooper previously met him when Stack delivered a lecture to the Royal Aeronautical Society in London on research being done by NASA into vertical lifting vehicles. Stack was rightly regarded as a world authority in this field at the time, and as Hooper described the P1127 project, he became most enthusiastic about its potential. NASA was looking at several of the many VTOL ideas around at that time including propellers, tilting wings, deflected slipstreams and so on, but the Hawker project was the first fighter configuration using jets. Better still, it looked beautifully simple.

To Hooper's surprise and delight Stack, without any prompting, ordered that a one-sixth scale, powered model should be made by his people to be tested in their free flight wind tunnel. It was the only one of its kind in the world and was radically different from the normal wind tunnel facility available to Hawker, where a model was set on a pedestal at given angles and numbers then read off about its behaviour. The NASA tunnel had four pilots sitting outside in cubicles watching the model through their windows, and actually flying it. One controlled yaw, another roll, another pitch and the last pilot was responsible for height. Between them, each

The 1/6th scale free-flight model of the P1127 being flown remotely in the wind tunnel by three different pilots during the NASA Langley trials, 1960.

concentrating on his particular axis of movement, the four pilots flew the 1127 model from the hover right through the transition into conventional wingborne flight.

Bill Bedford watched these tests with some apprehension. It was an uncanny experience in some respects, because he had never actually flown the airplane going through transitions as it was doing in that wind tunnel. He had often projected himself mentally through that flying phase, but here he was watching an exact scale model of the P1127 going successfully, if hesitantly, from jetborne to wingborne flight. It was rather like being gifted with second sight, but Bill did not find it a particularly comforting experience. He now confesses he was horrified by the way the aircraft behaved, but the NASA pilots flying it in concert from their little cubicles enthused about its characteristics. Compared to the other VTOL vehicles they'd been testing, the 1127 model behaved impeccably. Bedford shrugged, grinned at this information and made a mental note to avoid these other VTOL machines at all costs.

NASA had gone to a great deal of trouble to simulate the characteristics of the 1127. They had to build an ingenious little tip-driven fan inside the model with sufficient thrust to lift it vertically. A high pressure air line came down and exhausted the tips of the fan which gave it its propulsion. The thrust from the nozzles and the intake flow were a very close simulation of the full scale aircraft. From the very first flight, the model had no problems in either hovering or making the transition to wing-borne flight. Even for the professionals from Hawker, noting all the data, it was a fascinating experience to watch this modelmaker's dream being put through its paces.

It came as no surprise to Bill Bedford or Ralph Hooper that NASA recommended the control power of the aircraft be increased by 100 per cent. They had seen enough in the tunnel testing to convince them that when it came to hovering they would need to revise their calculations of how much power would be needed to bleed from the engine to operate the puffer valves successfully. The other part of their American experience reinforced their feelings. NASA provided them with a simulator into which they fed the known characteristics of the P1127. With hindsight, Bedford realizes it was much more demanding to fly than the P1127 ever was, but it underscored the need for more power in the reaction controls they were building into the prototype. To maintain control of the simulator, he was being forced into alarmingly big movements of the cockpit controls, and Bedford did not like it.

He found NASA's variable stability helicopter probably the most useful experience of his American visit. It had knobs in the back which allowed one to vary the parameters of control feel, control power, control sensitivity in roll, pitch and yaw. They were able to feed into the helicopter the curves of control power and sensitivity they had designed for the 1127, fly it, analyze the data, then change the flying characteristics of the helicopter and try it again. Obviously, it was not directly comparable with the 1127, but it was a vertical takeoff machine, and its infinitely variable characteristics did provide some information which was useful.

These were the positive aspects of the American visit, while the negative aspect came with the first crash of the P1127 program. Hawker test pilot Hugh Merewether, who was with Bill Bedford, almost wished it had been a P1127, for he experienced one of the test pilot's nightmares. He crashed someone else's research airplane, the little Bell X14. It had seemed perfectly logical in the happy spirit of cooperation prevailing at the time, for the two British test pilots to visit NASA at Ames Research Center and take a look at their X14. An intriguing aircraft, it was a mini example of vectored thrust. Two engines, with cascade deflectors mounted in each tailpipe, enabled the pilot to direct the thrust downwards for hovering flight and horizontally for conventional flying, and intermediate angles for transitions. It flew rather like a slow speed version of the P1127 and was designed originally without autostabilization. It also used reaction control jets for control in hover. The X14 had a Beech Mentor light aircraft wing, a Beech Bonanza tail, and low wing loading and a low stalling speed. At the time of the Hawker visit, it had two engines on either side of the fuselage. These engines were Bristol Siddeley Vipers, soon to be superseded by General Electric turbojet engines. The X14 which was sponsored by the United States Air Force never got beyond the stage of an experimental vehicle, despite talk at one time of trying to develop it into a supersonic V/STOL fighter. Nevertheless it was a fascinating machine. Not least because it eventually had variable stability built into its control system. This meant that it could be used to simulate the handling characteristics of other V/STOL aircraft before they had even flown, offering invaluable information to the designers. The attractions of the original X14 to the P1127 team were obvious.

Both Hawker pilots were thoroughly briefed on the X14's handling characteristics and takeoff procedure. Hugh Merewether was to make the first familiarization flight. He climbed into the open cockpit and sat there, following his briefing instructions, and burning off fuel until the engine thrust became greater than the aircraft's weight. The little airplane lifted off naturally and almost immediately started to oscillate uncontrollably and slid sideways into the runway. There was a rending crash, and the undercarriage broke. Merewether was unhurt though acutely embarrassed. Despite his flying experience he'd found that the stick movements necessary to control the X14, without autostabilization, were so large that he just could not hold it. It was, he said, a bit like a loose tooth. The important lesson for the embryo P1127 was that there would have to be much higher gearing from stick to reaction controls. The other lesson was that people can be surprisingly magnanimous about other people bending their little research aircraft. NASA told them that the airplane was going to be grounded anyway to have the more powerful engines fitted.

The American experience also convinced the pilots that simple controls were going to be important. There was a great deal of controversy in the design office over whether they should go for the helicopter type collective pitch control which looked rather crude, or whether they should hold out for a normal fighter throttle. The argument ran that as it was going to lift off like a helicopter, it made sense to have a lever like a helicopter in which you pulled up to operate the lift capability, then twisted it for normal forward flight.

Bill Bedford is an ex-fighter pilot and both he and Merewether were resolute that they did not want an agricultural lever in any Hawker fighter. They argued that no one had proved that you could not control the height with a well-engineered pilot's throttle operating conventionally, and with great sensitivity, by increasing or decreasing power in the hover. It was a battle, but with a mixture of tact and doggedness the pilot's point of view prevailed. In the ideal world the throttle would be tied up with the nozzle selector, but only at the expense of complexity and the possible risk to flight safety. No one has yet found a better way of resolving this than the two controls side by side in the neat throttle box.

The first prototype XP 831 was now recognizable in the workshops as an airplane and as 1960 advanced, preparations were being made for the first flight. Stanley Hooker had made the mistake of asking Sir Sydney Camm if he intended to make the maiden flight a conventional one with a normal takeoff and landing, nozzles pointing rearwards. Sir Sydney snapped: "Of course not. What would I want to do that for. Hawker airplanes always have marvellous flying qualities and this one will have them too. We'll go vertical on the first flight." It was a confidence, though, that in his inner self Sir

Sydney could not really have felt, for the flying qualities of his new aircraft in the VTOL mode were still very much unknown. His chief test pilot was continuing to arm himself with as much knowledge as possible. He did a full helicopter conversion course on the Hiller 2E and flew about thirty hours of vertical takeoff and landing on that. Helicopter flying went on regularly right up to the day before the first flight of the P1127. He also went to Belfast to make a few brief flights in the Short SC1.

The SC1 had been the darling of the U.K. aeronautical establishment for some years. It represented what to most people was the only viable way to perform VTOL—with separate engines for lift and propulsion. The theory was that, as both the lift and cruise engines had been designed to perform their separate roles at maximum efficiency, there were two major benefits. First, the combined weight of these engines was about the same as a single dual-purpose engine. Second, for strike aircraft, operating at sea level, the propulsion engine of the composite powerplant would use much less fuel than the single large lift-thrust engine which runs at a small fraction of its designed thrust in cruise and, therefore, uses more fuel.

Hawker had never seriously contemplated the multi-engine concept because of its complexity. The SC1 had four Rolls Royce RB 108 lightweight jet lift engines mounted vertically in side-by-side pairs around the center of gravity. A fifth RB 108 was installed in the rear fuselage for propulsion. The fact was, though, that the SC1 needed the thrust of all four lift engines for vertical takeoff or landing. Losing one meant 25 per cent less than total needs, and the airplane would descend rapidly from the skies. This was of academic importance to Bill Bedford's immediate plans because his flights were to be from the aircraft suspended from a gantry.

To understand the simplicity of the Harrier concept, it's interesting to consider the relative compexity of this airplane which had received several million pounds of government money as a research project—while the P1127 had been existing on private venture funds. The SC1 was the first attempt at putting wings and the traditional trappings of an airframe around the legendary Rolls Royce "Flying Bedstead"—the metal frame with two Rolls Royce Nene engines attached to it. Weighing approximately 800 pounds, the SC1 was a single seat, tailless delta wing aircraft with a large cockpit and excellent visibility. The cockpit layout was conventional, but its complexity, compared with the P1127, was mindboggling. The P1127 had only one extra control lever. On the other hand, the SC1 had four extra engines, each with its separate instruments for revolutions per minute and temperature. There were special starting systems for these lift engines which involved raising and lowering a device which allowed air into the intakes, and other complications. On the ground, before takeoff, it was helpful to have another pilot outside on radio going through a check list. The workload on a pilot re-lighting these engines on his own in flight, at the end of a sortie, can be imagined. In war, with battle damage and perhaps injury, to land such a complex aircraft safely could make enormous demands on a pilot.

Aside from this limitation, with its full autostabilization it was very pleasant to fly in the V/STOL mode. The control system was triplicated so that if one "lane" of the autostabilization failed, it would not have a great effect on control. The pilot could in a dire emergency override the electrical signals of the autostabilizer, by pulling an emergency lever. However, it was not an aircraft designed to be flown manually. Still, with its jet reaction control puffers similar to the P1127 it would sit beautifully in the hover. The big intake for the lift engines was mounted on top of the fuselage about the center of gravity, so the effect of all that air rushing into the intake did not disturb the airplane. Bedford only managed to squeeze a few minutes suspended from the gantry in the SC1, and felt it was of some use but of necessity limited. It gave him some feel for flying with full autostabilization, but that was not the name of the game he was going to be playing with the 1127.

While Bedford prepared himself for the first flight, the engineers worked on the engine. Noise was a serious problem at Dunsfold Airfield, and to keep complaints from the local populace to a minimum, a special concrete pen was built. The airplane sat in this pen over a deep pit which enabled the hot gases to escape, without "cooking" the underside of the airframe by reflecting the hot jets back from the ground. Enormous "thunderboxes" were wheeled up and fitted round the wing and against the fuselage. The roar of the Pegasus was not stilled, but its muted note kept complaints down. The local population had a perfect right to complain. At close range the sound of the Pegasus at full power sets up a frequency which can make the entire body flutter. The pre-flight engine testing was important to check that the fuselage was not going to become overheated and to make adjustments to engine and airframe.

The day of the first flight dawned. It was October 21, 1960, only eighteen months since the first drawings had been issued to the workshops and a remarkably speedy development from drawing board to first flight. Sir Sydney's terse prediction to Stanley Hooker that the first flight would be vertical was only partially true, though. He had scorned the gantry type of restricted operation which Short had been using for the SC1 in Belfast, but the Ministry of Defense, the safety overlords, insisted that Hawker restrain the new aircraft in some way. To Sir Sydney's chagrin, they insisted that the P1127 could only attempt to hover, restrained by tethers. These were ropes attached to wing tips and nose. The aircraft was to hover over a gridded pit, and the ends of these ropes were threaded through the grid and attached to a number of big cast iron discs on the bottom of the pit. The theory was that as the aircraft lifted up, it tried to pull up more rope and in doing so lifted more and more of the weights, thus applying a gentle restraining force. The tethers were intended to give no more than a few feet of vertical or sideways motion. Sir Sydney was never a man to concede that Whitehall bureaucrats had any sensible suggestions to make. At the end of the first few flights though, he was secretly relieved that the restrictions had been imposed on full, free hovering flight.

The aircraft which stood above the grid that morning was almost fish-like in appearance. It looked extremely purposeful, but it was short, stubby and ugly. The P1127 was just over forty-one feet in length and stood just ten feet three inches high. From tip to tip, its wings, with their forty-five degrees swept leading edge, measured only twenty-four feet four inches. The cockpit was right in the nose and just aft were the enormous bulbous intakes of the Pegasus engine. The two front jet nozzles sprouted behind the intakes and the rear pair lay below the straight trailing edge of the wings.

Chief Test Pilot Bedford stood amongst the small group of engineers and designers gathered on the tarmac at Dunsfold to watch final preparation. Bedford had been seduced by the sheer aestheticism of test-flying the graceful Hunter, and he viewed prototype XP831 with mixed feelings. It was difficult to love this odd-looking aircraft, but he consoled himself with the thought that the test pilot's career is a short one, and the chance to lead the flying program on a new concept is uncommon enough. To be the first man to fly a revolutionary machine was a crowning achievement to any test pilot's career. The thoughts that flickered through his mind at that time were occupying the others like Ralph Hooper too. Would this airplane ever get any further than any of the many other esoteric attempts there had been around the world? Apart from the Hunter, still selling well, all the company's eggs at that moment were firmly placed inside the basket marked P1127. This was not a mere research vehicle, but an aircraft that they needed to get into production. It was now around mid-day and the strong smell of aircraft fuel focused their attention on the more immediate problem. Would the airplane lift off the ground in the first place? The casual onlooker might have regarded bleakly the auguries of success of this aviation milestone. The man in the flying overalls was quite definitely hobbling. His right leg was in plaster.

A few days before the first flight was due, Bedford had been in Germany flying a demonstration of the Hunter two-seater. Returning to his hotel in the evening, his driver failed to negotiate a bend and ran into some trees. A German doctor with Teutonic efficiency slapped an enormous, cumbersome plaster on his leg and told him to keep it on for four months. It seemed certain that Bedford was to be denied the historic first flight for which he had done so much preparation.

However, tenacity is a well-known prerequisite of the test pilot. Fired by a sense of determination and impending history, Bedford spent the few days remaining, cramming in as many hours of dual flying as he could get in every aircraft type he could be heaved into, including gliders and helicopters. The Royal Air Force's Central Medical Board was his target, in particular the current president, an old friend and a distinguished aviation medicine pioneer from the Institute of Aviation Medicine, Group Captain Pat Ruffle-Smith. He was responsible for signing the crucial piece of paper, the passport which would clear him for the first flight, or ground him. Bedford brought along witnesses and written statements to back up the variety of machines he had proven capable of controlling. The Board indulged him, and Ruffle-Smith issued him with a medical category unique in aviation history: "fit, civil test pilot, tethered hovering only." Bedford resisted a strong impulse to hug the president of the Board, settled for his secretary instead, and hopped out of the room!

Every single piece of equipment not considered abso-

lutely vital to that first flight had been removed from the aircraft. At that early state of its development the Pegasus engine was producing only 11,000 pounds of thrust. To get it
off the ground vertically, even with a small amount of fuel,
they reckoned they'd have to lose about 700 pounds of
weight, before the thrust could hope to exceed what remained. Out came the radio sets, undercarriage fairings and
jacks, nose boom, air brake, tail parachute installation, ram
air turbine and cabin-conditioning equipment. The glass windscreen was replaced with perspex. This gave the aircraft, with
pilot but no fuel, a weight of 9,243 pounds. In theory, this
allowed fuel for a maximum of three minutes hovering at
four hundred pounds of fuel per side. Obviously, though,
they would not have dreamt of running the fuel down to
zero, so the time airborne was clearly going to be very short.

Bedford hopped up the steps into the cockpit and was
strapped in. As the cockpit canopy closed over his head with
a clunk, he noticed that peculiar smell of oil and hot metal
now familiar to every Harrier pilot. As soon as new pilots
learn that it does not mean the airplane is on fire, they tend
to carry it in their senses as a mental association with the aircraft. Bedford started his checks. Instrumentation was relatively sparse at that stage. It was restricted to the dials necessary for hovering, which included jet pipe temperature, fan
r.p.m. and bearing temperature, and most important of all, at
that stage, fuel for port and starboard tanks. He started up
and sat there for some time, the engine churning, burning off
fuel, and familiarizing himself completely with his new environment. He'd sat in the cockpit before, of course, during
shop development work, and engine running tests, but this
time it was for "lift-off."

Now he was on his own and though his stomach was
tightening slightly in anticipation of opening the throttle,
there was a strangely heightened sense of enjoyment when he
thought of the watchers on the runway and the thousands

more in the company's factories whose hopes depended on
the flight tests he was about to start. His eyes scanned the
instruments in a thorough cockpit check. On the periphery of
his vision, he could see the bizarre sight of a man with a red
flag ready to warn him of any impending disaster on takeoff.
It was a sharp reminder that they were just passing into the
Stone Age of V/STOL.

The prototype did have limited, 20 per cent autostabilization in both pitch and roll as a pilot aid, and one of the
final checks which had to be made through the telephone line
with the ground crew since the radios had been removed, was
to confirm that this was operating. The autostabilization assisted the control movements of the jet puffers at the aircraft
extremities when they came into play as the main jet nozzles
were lowered. To check that the autostabilization was functioning before that, Bedford switched it on and moved stick
and rudder around. A ground observer confirmed that the
normal control surfaces of ailerons and tailplane were react-
ing in the correct sense. The fuel state was now down to 220
pounds per side. Bedford lowered the nozzles to an angle of
eighty-two degrees to the fuselage and opened the throttle.

There was a definite reluctance for the wheels to clear
the ground as the throttle advanced. It was sweaty in the
cockpit without any air conditioning, and Bedford's hands
were damp inside his gloves as he felt the wheels dragging and
scraping on the grid. Then the aircraft seemed to somehow
come to life. There was a definite lightening of the undercarriage, and the pilot felt a surprising excitement as the P1127
rose. Thrust had exceeded weight. It only rose a foot above
ground before the tethers restrained it, but it hovered for one
minute and forty-five seconds and Bill Bedford's tentative
control movements suggested that it had some degree of control. However, as they were to discover on the second flight,
there was a serious lack of control power because the engine
at that stage needed all it could muster to lift off vertically.

The first P1127 in a steady hover in October 1960, about twelve inches off the ground. The restraining tethers are attached to weights underneath the gridded platform at Dunsfold Aerodrome.

The prototype sitting there in the hover, though, had no more aerodynamic stability than a flying brick. It was crying out for more power for the controlling puffers at its extremities.

They increased the tethers to four feet, and the problems began. The gridded hovering platform had been placed in the middle of a very slight slope which meant that the P1127 always sat with one wing slightly low. It had not occurred to anyone that this would pose a problem, but it did. As soon as the throttle was opened fully the aircraft rose on the main undercarriage, leaning to starboard. It started cavorting around the nose wheel "like a drunken cow," and sliding sideways. As power was increased, the aircraft started to lift then dipped towards the lower wing. Control power was not sufficient to bring the wings level before the airplane pulled against the tethering system. Bedford was not in any real danger because of the restraints, but the airplane was uncontrollable. People scratched their heads and muttered, "Perhaps it's Bill's plastered leg that's causing it!" They solved the problem by putting spring-loaded skids under the outriggers, which adjusted to keep the wings level. Bedford's broken leg was vindicated.

Between November 3, 1960 and November 19, 1960 they carried out twenty-one tethered hovering sorties. It was becoming clearer with every sortie that something was going to have to be done fairly soon about the power of the vital reaction control system. It was exceptionally difficult to control it directionally, in yaw, and part of the problem was obviously caused by the yaw puffer also serving as a pitching control. All they had done up until then had been to demonstrate that they could hover the aircraft. But they really wanted to hover freely, unrestrained by tethers, and before they would be allowed to do that, it had to be demonstrated that Bedford could offer some measure of control. The test he set himself was to hover accurately, within these tethered confines, so accurately that he would not pull against the restraining ropes.

Rather like a modern fencer has his success or failure measured by electric impulse, so the airplane tethers were connected to microswitches. These were to illuminate lights on the ground whenever the machine pulled against a tether. Film cameras were set up to record the exercise and prototype number XP 831 lifted off. It was a remarkable display of sensitive control throughout all the control axes, and after a very few sorties, Bedford was hovering the airplane to within confines of a foot, without a flicker from these lights on the ground. The way was clear for the first free hover, which took place on November 19, the day after Bill's fortieth birthday. He recalls it: "It was like freeing a bird from a cage. At last we were rid of those horrible, irritating restraints." It

XP831, the first P1127 aircraft, flying in 1963. This historic aircraft survived over twelve years of testing and now occupies an honored spot in the Sir Sydney Camm Memorial Hall of the R.A.F. Museum, Hendon, United Kingdom.

meant they now could plan to explore the aircraft's potential further or expand the "flight envelope."

The undercarriage of an aircraft is not the most immediately stirring part of the equipment, but not much landing or taking off can be done without one. Sir Sydney Camm took a particular interest in the taxiing trials which led up to the first conventional flights of the 1127. Remember his predictions about undercarriage legs snapping like carrots? His prediction came true—only it wasn't the hated outrigger legs which came to grief, but the strong main undercarriage leg under the fuselage. The P1127 was using the same wheels and brakes as the Seahawk fighter and every time the brakes were applied there was a moderate shudder. On February 4, 1961, during braking there was a sharp snapping sound, the aircraft subsided, and an ominous pool of red hydraulic fluid dripped from the shattered oleo. Quite a bit of headscratching produced the theory that the brake pads, which had been diametrically opposed, had set up an excitation in the leg which had led to the fracture. Changing the brake pads around solved that problem, and on March 6th, they took the airplane from Dunsfold to the Royal Aircraft Establishment at Bedford for more taxi-ing trials.

They took it up to speeds of around 150 knots along the runway and started to run into significant problems. The undercarriage manufacturers had told them that they had tested the outrigger wheels at up to 200 knots without experiencing any "shimmy" effects. However, ground observers, in the preliminary taxi trials, had reported what they thought was a "shimmy" effect from the castering action of the outrigger wheels. Bill Bedford himself thought he felt it though he failed to set it off properly even with deliberate running over rough ground at Dunsfold. The trials continued with runs at increasing speed to check nose wheel steering, braking effect and brake temperatures.

One day at around 160 knots there was a noise like a cannon going off, and the whole airplane vibrated violently. He shut the throttle and put the brakes on. It had been classic outrigger shimmy, and when Bedford stepped out, he could see its zig-zag pattern of molten rubber streaked down the runway. The oscillating wheel had eventually burst the tire. The undercarriage manufacturers blamed the entire episode on the burst tire and it seemed to be settling into a "chicken or egg" situation until it was finally agreed that it had happened like this. When the outrigger was in contact with the ground there was a damping effect, but if the aircraft lifted off slightly during its high speed taxi run, then this damping was reduced and shimmy set in. When the outrigger touched down again there was no way of stopping the violent oscillating motion. They cured the problem by fitting the outriggers with shear pins which would break and allow the wheels to caster only when the loads became excessive. As an interim measure, they were prepared to accept that the tires would scrub and scrape a bit on the runway during landing and ground maneuvering.

The Harrier of today has superb nosewheel steering. Pilots have described it as the only jet with Grand Prix driving characteristics. However, in the run-up to those first conventional flights, they were struggling with something much less sophisticated. Hawker had not been involved much with nosewheel steering before, but they talked to various experts and finally settled on the system used by a civil aircraft, the Argosy. This was all very well for the Argosy which carried only 10 per cent of its weight on the nosewheel. The P1127 carried 30 per cent. They discovered that the only way they could control the aircraft was not to have the system continuously engaged, but just to "blip" it as required with a prod of the appropriate rudder to help change direction. When it came to takeoffs, even conventional takeoffs when they would not normally have had the jet nozzles down, they had to put them down to bring the reaction control puffers into play for extra steering control. It was a mixture of experience, ingenuity and a fair bit of trial and error. The next hurdle would be the first conventional flight. Beyond that lay the real goal: to make the prototype fly from hovering flight to fully wingborne flight and then back again.

The prelude to the transitions was the first conventional flight on March 13, 1961. After the flight, Hawker's public relations department had issued the bland statement to the press: "The airplane handled beautifully and has a great potential." In pilot's language that meant that it was rough and noisy and had enough faults to make it the ideal trainer for new test pilots! Preparations for the first conventional flights were thorough because both engine and airframe were still unknown quantities in conventional flight. The insurance against a forced landing was to fly many hours in a Hunter simulating as near as they could, the lift-drag ratio of the P1127. They put down the undercarriage and the flaps in flight to try to provide drag qualities similar to the proto-type. They also did a series of takeoffs simulating engine fail-ure from the moment they had flying speed, right down to the last possible minute they could have an engine failure on takeoff and still stream the tail parachute and get away with it. They also planned the first conventional flight around four of the longest runways in the country on a circular flight to give them a sporting chance of getting it down in one piece if anything went wrong. They even did simulated forced land-ings at these four airfields and worked out emergency radio frequencies with them. They could do no more.

The brief on that first conventional flight was simple; get it up, and get it down in one piece. Bill Bedford took off with about half fuel accompanied by a chase Hunter. He left the undercarriage down until he passed through 500 feet, so that if there were to be any big trim change when it was raised, he would have plenty of height to sort it out. There was no lack of adrenalin in the cockpit, for the lack of funds during development had meant that this prototype had not been able to benefit from the usual wind tunnel testing which could have given more accurate predictions of its flight char-acteristics. The instrument recorders were running inside the aircraft, as Bedford climbed to 25,000 feet and pushed the speed up to around 400–450 knots, .8 Mach number. As he climbed, he carried out some basic tests of its flying charac-teristics, centering the stick laterally and longitudinally, and doing gentle turns to get a feel for the stick forces. There were severe engine limitations and Bedford had marked the instruments accordingly. They read, "Avoid 43 to 54 per cent fan r.p.m. and 69–77 r.p.m. Don't throttle back below 77 per cent fan r.p.m. above .7 Mach." So, when he wanted to slow down he had little freedom to throttle back.

Frequently, he had to decelerate the airplane by turning or putting out the airbrake. Two pleasant characteristics emerged though. Lateral control was superb. With its powerful ailerons, the airplane was almost begging to be rolled. He pulled the nose up, moved the stick and around she went, quick as a flash. Straight and level, then a roll in the opposite direction. The climb, acceleration, and general agility were equally invigorating. Despite its other failings, Bedford could have put on an air display there and then. He discovered at a safe height that when the flaps were lowered it caused a severe nose down pitch, so the landing was a long flat approach without flaps.

The flight had been another important step forward, but clearly there were a lot of problems to solve. Some of them could be directly attributed to the airframe being built around the large engine. All that jet disturbance was blasting under the wing and impinging on the tail, which did nothing to help the aircraft's longitudinal problems. The unique nature of the design was to give the designers a continuing headache for a long time to come because of the difficulties of resolving three fundamentals—the center of gravity, the center of thrust, and the center of lift. In an ideal world the center of thrust (all that power being poured out via the two jet nozzles on either side) would coincide with the center of gravity, and there would be no inherent imbalance to contend with. In practice, this proved impossible, and as the power of the Pegasus grew, the problems became more obtuse. The headache was that if they moved the center of gravity far enough forward to get the stability right for conventional flight with nozzles horizontal, then it would be too far away from the thrust center when the nozzles were vertical for landing and takeoff. The result was that the reaction control system was demanding so much air from the engines to keep the aircraft trimmed in VTOL, that it could scarcely muster enough thrust to get off the ground. More of how they unscrambled that one, later.

That first conventional flight lasted twenty-two minutes, and over the next week or so they carried out regular conventional flights. They made as many as three in one day on March 15. It said a lot for the serviceability of the prototype which was joined by the second prototype XP 836 on July 7, 1961. They were now working up to the acid test of the transitional flights. Hugh Merewether and Bill Bedford worked together on the joint conventional flying program on XP 836 and intensive hovering sorties on XP 831. By this stage the variable bleed reaction control system was devised and fitted to both aircraft. It gave a large and very welcome boost in control power while keeping the engine temperature down by reducing the demands on it. Compared to other programs like the SC1, the rate of progress had been remarkable so far. It was only six months from the first conventional flight to the first transitions.

A major step along that path was achieved when one of the aircraft flew down the length of the runway at Dunsfold at a height of fifty feet and a speed of fifty knots, stopped, and put itself down vertically on a prearranged spot. It may not sound like much, but it showed that the aircraft had enough thrust, enough control to lift off and fly at a constant height with complete control and place itself down at a point of the pilot's choosing. The nozzles had only been deflected slightly from the vertical to gain some forward flying speed. It was all happening in a gradual way. Progressively, one of the prototypes was slowing down in conventional flight to below stalling speed, at around ninety knots, and investigating the airplane's behaviour as it came to the threshold of hovering. The other was practicing vertical lift-offs and accelerating progressively, with nozzles slightly aft, towards ninety knots. These were in fact narrowing the gap between the two ends of the transition spectrum. On September 12, the gap was bridged.

There was a small group of watchers on the ground at Dunsfold at nine o'clock that morning; people like Ralph Hooper and John Fozard and others who'd been heavily involved in the airframe and engine design. There was a light breeze whipping across the runways and the group stood fairly close together as Bill Bedford climbed into the aircraft astride the hovering grid. It is not possible to overestimate the importance of what was to happen. Of course, the first hovers had been interesting, even exciting, but in retrospect, it would have been a little surprising if the thrust had not exceeded the weight and caused a vertical lift-off. This was something different. It was the crucial test of the new concept. Like most aircraft designers few of the watching group had much, if any, piloting experience themselves. To put your creation in the hands of another human being in this way evokes a strange feeling of impotence and excitement combined.

For the pilots, it was almost an anticlimax. After all they had been getting closer and closer to the transition for weeks now, so there were not likely to be any great unknowns awaiting Bill Bedford as he opened the throttle. He lifted off to a considerable height above the grid, executed a pirouette and accelerated from jetborne flight into an unexpectedly smooth transition to wingborne flight. As he moved the nozzles to the horizontal, the acceleration was instantaneous. The aircraft disappeared from view, and the watchers burst into spontaneous cheering. It was a marvellous moment —the summation of a lot of brainpower and sweat by a lot of people.

To minimize workload, Bedford's return to the airfield was by conventional landing. Hugh Merewether then did an exact repeat flight in the same aircraft. Next came a conventional takeoff followed by a decelerating transition from wingborne to jetborne flight, and a vertical landing. Then they demonstrated the aircraft's control in both accelerating and decelerating transitions in the same flight—both with and, significantly, without autostabilization.

There is a footnote to that historic day which should delight anyone who enjoys putting one over on the establishment. The Ministry of Aviation was of course providing limited funding for the project by that time. Hawker was told they would have to wait for their flight test reports to be thoroughly studied and approved, before what was effectively government property should be risked in this highly unusual way. But, the man from the Ministry was slow in putting in an appearance, and the P1127 team was impatient to prove their concept. Bedford was given the nod by one of his directors that if he and the flight development team were happy, then he should go ahead and do it without official permission. The Ministry, of course, had to be informed that transitions had taken place, and it caused great amusement when their letter of congratulation said: "We understand from the chief test pilot that it happened by accident—that he was accelerating along the runway so rapidly that it was safer to carry out a transition than to slow down." There was no harm done, and it stirred that latent, naughty schoolboy which lurks inside most grown men—even chief test pilots.

A bit of levity is very good for the soul of men who are wrestling with such serious problems, and even after moments of danger, pilots like Bedford were prepared to take a joke against themselves. The story of the McGregor turn is a case in point. Early on in the test flying program one of the Hawker directors was so enthusiastic to show off the prototype that he insisted on bringing along no less a person than Air Marshal McGregor, the Commander in Chief of Fighter Command. McGregor was one of the people who would have to be eventually convinced that P1127 was an aircraft his pilots should be flying in front line service. Bedford was most unhappy about this. The development flying was still at an early stage, and he did not want to risk spoiling the image. He was overruled, and the Air Marshal turned up at Dunsfold to watch the P1127 put through its paces.

Bedford took off vertically, inclined the nozzles slightly rearwards and accelerated away from the grid at about forty knots. He tried to do a turn, and the aircraft seemed to accelerate in yaw and pirouetted around. He kicked on full opposite rudder, but it did not make any difference. The aircraft twirled around several times in this impromptu aerial ballet, quite out of control. Eventually, the opposite rudder took effect and the aircraft limped off down the runway with the pilot applying full aileron to correct sideslip. The distinguished visitor seemed to think it was all part of the demonstration! Afterwards some wag dubbed it the McGregor turn, and Bedford joined in the laughter. But it had been his first introduction to a phenomenon with great potential danger, known as intake momentum drag yaw.

This was the problem. At speeds between thirty and one hundred knots, before the fin of the airplane was giving directional stability, the airplane was directionally unstable and suffered from the enormous amounts of air rushing into the intakes which are well ahead of the center of gravity. This intake drag tended to cause the aircraft to yaw and a strong rolling effect also developed. Unless the pilot could keep the aircraft straight, the rolling moment could build into something quite outside the capacity of his ailerons to hold it.

The team decided that the only way to solve this problem was to deliberately induce the condition. They did liftoffs and then translated sideways at progressive speeds up to sixty knots, and nothing untoward happened. Next, they tried turns, and on one sortie, Bedford was doing a turn at sixty knots, 200 feet above the Compasses Pub, on the edge

of the airfield. Suddenly, he had full aileron on to counter-
act a wing low effect, and he felt just like an apple balanced
very precariously on top of a barrow. He recalled: "It was a
go, no-go situation. Make a mistake and you've had it at that
height." He had instinctively cranked on the correct aileron,
but he had to think very carefully before he applied rudder.
Very slowly he fed on rudder, bit by bit. It was the correct
side. He had control.*

John Farley, later to be Chief Test Pilot, frequently
demonstrated at air shows and flying demonstrations that
almost anything could be done with the Harrier in the hover.
Although he did it with his series of coordinated "S" turns with
a large amount of bank on, Farley knew better than anyone
that he must obey the rules which earlier pilots like Bedford
learned the hard way.

Within a month of the first transitions, Bedford and
Merewether were investigating the aircraft's characteristics in
the short takeoff mode accelerating the airplane along the
runway with nozzles horizontal, then putting them down and
jumping into the air. These first short takeoffs showed dramatically the potential of the P1127 to increase its payload
over its vertical takeoff capability, with even a short takeoff
run. Short takeoff with full load, and wing lift aided by lift
from the deflected jet nozzles, then a return to base by
vertical landing was the key to the future military operation
of the Harrier.

On December 12, somewhere over the south of England, there was a loud bang as the prototype XP 836 flew
supersonically in a dive. It was the first time a V/STOL aircraft had achieved supersonic speed. As the aircraft went past
the speed of sound, the wing low effect which Bedford had

---

*The present aircraft has limited authority autostabilization in
yaw, pitch and roll. Buzzers on the rudder pedals tell the pilot which to
apply if sideslip develops in that critical speed range. We'll look at this
development later.

been controlling, with about three-quarters aileron, righted itself. It was a good feeling to have flown an airplane which could fly backwards at one end of the speed range and supersonically at the other. Though the aircraft was still, in Bedford's words "a bit of a heap to fly," they had in fact fully expanded the flight envelope. Two days later XP 836 was destroyed in a crash, and Bedford was lucky to escape with his life.

It was a routine conventional flight to test airframe "flutter" by deliberately inducing vibrations in the airframe. Bedford flew the aircraft at increasing speeds, sharply displacing the stick with a little metal "bonker" to give a crisp input. At a speed of 525 knots he pulled up from this condition and throttled back to around 400 knots. Suddenly, passing through 5,000 feet, there was a marked roaring noise and general airframe and engine roughness. The airplane decelerated, quickly shedding one hundred knots. Bedford was close to the Royal Naval Air Station at Yeovilton in Somerset and decided to carry out a precautionary landing there. Hugh Merewether was in the chase Hunter but could not see anything immediately wrong, though he did have his hands full clearing the emergency landing with Yeovilton.

Bedford was cleared to land on runway 27 and started final approach at around 200 knots. The undercarriage was lowered successfully but the flaps would not extend fully at that speed, and a small wing low effect started to develop. He controlled it with a small amount of stick, but at 200 feet as the speed came down to 170 knots, the situation deteriorated and he found himself with the stick hard over. He could not prevent the aircraft wanting to roll slowly to the left. It was a horrible feeling. The altimeter was unwinding. As a last ditch effort, he fed on more power, to increase speed and, he hoped, control, but the roll simply worsened.

It was time to get out. For some reason he changed hands, and, keeping the stick hard over with his left hand, he yanked the ejection seat handle between his legs with the other. There was a loud bang and the seat smashed through the canopy above his head. It was a perfect ejection. There was a sharp tug as the parachute opened and almost at once he was on the ground. Two or three seconds longer in the aircraft, and his parachute would not have had time to open.

Bedford had never been closer to death. A few hundred yards away the million pound prototype was blazing in a barn. He picked up his stopwatch which had been thrown clear. An Admiral's personal helicopter from the Naval Air Station flew to the crash scene and picked Bedford up. He recalls being very concerned about his muddy flying boots spoiling the superb thick blue carpet in the V.I.P. helicopter. John Dale, then Assistant Chief Engineer on the Pegasus program, heard about the crash and drove the few miles from Bristol to Yeovilton. He found Bedford languidly sipping a drink and asked him if he was injured in any way. Bedford told him: "They ran from that helicopter and insisted on bundling me on to a stretcher to carry me to the helicopter. My dear chap, I could have fallen off and hurt myself!"

What had caused the crash? The black box flight recorder showed peculiar traces of profound vibration on the port side of the aircraft, though Bedford insisted that the engine seemed to be working perfectly. A few days after the crash the mystery was solved. A farmer picked up a strange yellow object in his orchard some distance from the crash scene. It was the port front Pegasus nozzle, which had broken off in flight. Had Bedford known he lost one of them, he would never have attempted to put his flaps down. As he reduced speed, two nozzles were blowing on one flap and on the other side there was only one. The result was to induce that uncontrollable roll. The front nozzles until then had been made of light weight glass fiber reinforced plastic, and this had saved one hundred pounds in overall weight. There was no question of retaining those, and the engine designers went straight for steel.

By the end of 1961, Hawker and Bristol had proved that the new airplane worked, but there was a great deal of development work still to be done. The little aircraft which Ralph Hooper had sketched out only four years before had come to life and proved that this simple approach to V/STOL worked. But the 1127 was still some way from being a viable military fighting machine. Some dismissed it as a toy which could not carry a cigarette packet from one side of a playing field to the other. The thrust exceeded the aircraft's weight by a bit more than that, but continued development of the Pegasus engine was clearly of paramount importance if the airplane was ever going to make it into full scale production.

Chapter 5

The P1154, a Contest Winner

During 1960 and 1961 Hawker was busy proving, through test flying and continuous development, that their new concept worked in technical terms. However, the battle also had to be waged on another and equally important front of political and military feasibility. On that front the new airplane was steadily losing ground. The Royal Air Force's Operational Requirements Branch had in effect "had their arms twisted" by the Ministry of Supply to give British industry some encouragement by writing a requirement for the qualities they would want from any operational version of the P1127. This was formulated during 1960 and 1961 and was known as Operational Requirement 345 (OR 345). However, the R.A.F. frankly did not consider the P1127 as a serious military proposition. At a meeting, just five days after the first tethered hovering of the airplane on October 21, 1960, the Air Staff stressed its shortcomings, e.g., tiny payload capability, not enough engine thrust. All that the designers could honestly reply was that they were hopeful of improving the performance.

Their biggest foe at that time was the Rolls Royce Engine Company, who ironically, since the merger with Bristol in 1967 are now the manufacturer of the Pegasus. At that time, however, Bristol Engines was independent, and the deadly rival of Rolls Royce. Rolls Royce told the Air Staff that aircraft of the SC1 type, using their multi-engine approach, could offer everything the P1127 could, and much more, including the bewitching inducement of supersonic performance. Hawker's philosophy up until then had been that supersonic performance was unnecessary because their aircraft was designed for a ground attack role. But, many senior officers in the Air Staff were uninterested in any front line aircraft which couldn't go through the sound barrier—irrespective of its role.

The name of Rolls Royce has always been synonomous with excellence in many people's minds. It was an image that Rolls Royce had quite justifiably cultivated, and when it came to playing politics—lobbying, briefing and so on—they had no equal in the British aircraft industry. There was, at that time, what was wryly referred to as a Rolls Royce "mafia," who concentrated on this area of political and military influence. They were very successful at it, too. It wasn't a question of professional jealousy between the different programs. It was simply that Rolls Royce and the Hawker/Bristol partnership were each equally convinced that their road to V/STOL was the right one.

Apart from the political lobbying, there were learned technical papers published by both sides stressing the advantages of their concept and the shortcomings of the other. Rolls Royce, however, never tried to defend the multi-engine concept on the grounds of simplicity which Hawker, with vectored thrust, felt was the P1127's most potent strength. The prize for Rolls Royce was a glittering one. Although the SC1 was only a research aircraft, if they could convince the right people that the basic concept was right, then the first operational V/STOL aircraft would fly that way, using their engines. There was a steady stream of Royal Air Force officers visiting the Hawker factory at Kingston, and it was fairly obvious that a number of them had had the "Rolls Royce treatment." They were exceptionally well-briefed on what Rolls had identified and published as the "drawbacks" of the vectored thrust principle.

However, Hawker still had funding from the government Ministry of Supply for six aircraft, and work continued steadily on test flying and development, particularly on ways of improving engine thrust. It was the lack of engine thrust particularly which was keeping them from meeting the goals of OR 345. At the beginning of 1961, a new and radical development suggested itself. The Republic Aviation Company in America and Fokkers in Holland got together to try to meet a NATO requirement called General Operating Requirement 2. It was a guideline to what NATO thought their next generation fighting airplane ought to be and eventually became NATO Basic Military Requirement 3. Out of the discussions these two companies had with Bristol, came the Bristol suggestion to increase the thrust of the Pegasus by burning fuel in the front nozzles which was the equivalent of re-heat in a conventional jet engine. Sketches were drawn at Kingston, around a Pegasus, with front nozzle burning. It appeared it would easily give a V/STOL aircraft supersonic performance. Hawker gave this paper airplane the designation P1150, but they decided at that stage to make no official noises about it.

Their reasoning was sound. To dangle the prospect of supersonic performance before the Air Staff at that time based on an idea that had not even left the drawing board, might well mean the operational requirement for the P1127 would be withdrawn, after all their development effort. Besides, it looked as if they had cracked the problem of engine thrust anyway. Stanley Hooker had come up with an engine with a three stage fan which he promised would produce

18,000 pounds of thrust—the Pegasus 5. It now seemed certain that the P1127 would meet the most critical sortie requirements of the Air Staff. Sure enough they even extracted a piece of paper from the Air Staff conceding this. Unfortunately, their joy was short-lived, because very soon after, the operational requirement for the P1127 was withdrawn, on the grounds of "cost." The real reason was that the Air Staff reckoned the solution was closer with the multi-lift engine concept. The Rolls Royce lobby had indeed been effective! The success of the airplane which was to evolve into the Harrier owes little to the confidence and faith of Britain's aeronautical establishment in those early days. The prophets were finding little honor in their own land.

It was a bitter and serious blow for Hawker who had invested so much time and money in the project, but they still had funding for the six aircraft, and development continued. Had it not done so, had Hawker decided to abandon the project in the face of this official indifference, then there would have been no Harrier today. For although their next step along the road was to bid for a supersonic V/STOL fighter, that eventually was to founder. With hindsight, had they not carried on the development of the little subsonic aircraft, then they would have been left at the end of the day with nothing but some limited experience in the field and nothing concrete in the way of an operational aircraft.

In March 1961 NATO's requirements for a new V/STOL close support fighter had hardened into NBMR 3. This gave rise to NBMR 4, calling for a V/STOL transport aircraft to supply this new fighter operating from dispersed sites. The fighter was to be supersonic, and Hawker seized this opportunity to keep themselves in with a fighting chance of actually going into production with a V/STOL aircraft. After all, they had built up all this experience with the 1127. They had hovered, they had flown conventionally and they were soon to do the all-important transitions. Unlike the other competitors, the French and Germans, they were able to claim a wealth of practical experince, and in the "paper" airplane, the P1150, they had a basis to work from. Design work continued on the proposed engine, the BS 100, with plenum chamber burning of fuel in the front nozzles, and the engine looked as if it would produce 33,000 pounds of thrust. The Hawker entry for NBMR 3, the P1154, was submitted on January 10, 1962.

It was rather a bizarre sort of contest, because not one of the competing European countries had actually promised to buy the winning aircraft. It was just vaguely assumed that the prize for the winner would be vast orders for his aircraft. The main competitor to the P1154 was the French Mirage IIIV. Although both were still at the drawing board stage, Hawker could point to the success of their P1127, and the French to the flight trials of the Balzac, the forerunner to the Mirage IIIV.

The Balzac and later the Mirage IIIV used multiple engines for lift and cruise. These aircraft were the manifestation of all the persuasive argument that Rolls had been pouring into the ears of the British aeronautical establishment. In fact the Mirage was really a grown-up Short SC1, based on the conventional Mirage supersonic fighter. It had a delta wing, long thin tapering fuselage, and a stack of eight Rolls Royce RB 162 engines embedded in the center of the fuselage and a separate propulsion engine. It had arisen in the first place from a French Air Staff invitation of 1958 for a V/STOL subsonic tactical fighter for dispersed use during atomic war. General Aeronautique Marcel Dassault had submitted two proposals in 1959, of which the multi-engine concept was chosen in preference to a Harrier-type configuration using a single Pegasus engine.

The Hawker concept had always been directed towards simplicity, and their experience of transitions in the P1127 flying had supported that thinking. However, transitions from hover to wingborne flight for the Balzac and Mirage IIIV did little for the pilots' peace of mind. They took off with the vertical engines, housed in the fuselage, pointing straight down. They then opened up the horizontal engine for conventional flight and in effect, started taking off along a runway one hundred feet up. But as the nose came up to get wing lift for conventional flight, the lift engines, which were still partially supporting the aircraft, started pointing slightly forward. Therefore, at the time when the pilot wanted to go faster, the lift engines slowed him down. The answer was to climb several hundred feet then dive to complete the transition. Well, it was one way of doing it.

In April 1962, the NATO staff's technical evaluation committee announced their decision on NBMR 3. The British P1154 was declared the technical winner, but in an obvious attempt to placate the fierce nationalistic/political/military factions in NATO, they hedged their bets by saying that the Mirage was of "equal merit." An attempt was made by NATO to get international collaboration on a V/STOL project but the French went their own way and went on to develop the IIIV. The Royal Air Force now sat up and started to take an interest in V/STOL. Here in the P1154 was something that really looked useful. It was like a two-times P1127, with twice the thrust, twice the speed, twice the weight, twice the performance. They tried not to be concerned with the cost at this stage. The British government ordered the boards of the two aviation services, R.A.F. and Royal Navy, to write operational requirements around the performance of the P1154.

There was now to some extent a conflict of interest in Hawker. Here with the P1154 was an airplane admittedly still at drawing board stage, but an airplane which promised the most marvellous future for the company in home and overseas sales. Nevertheless, the P1127 program was continuing, though in a very low key way for fear of harming the supersonic project in any way. One of the developments which had helped keep interest alive in the P1127, despite the lack of an operational requirement by R.A.F., was an international agreement between Britain, America and Germany, to assess V/STOL through a tripartite squadron equipped with P1127's. It was a fascinating and important phase in the aircraft's development which we will examine in detail in the next chapter. The P1127 was the star of the international Farnborough Air Show in the summer of 1962, when one journalist reported, "Bill Bedford exhibited the stability and precision with which the P1127 can be maneuvered through an incredible angle, from a backward climb at twenty-four knots to absolutely motionless hovering and flat maneuvering around 360 degrees laterally while hovering over a fixed spot." It was a pity, Hawker felt, that the people who bought military aircraft did not share the excitement of the crowd.

Once a pilot has flown a Harrier he usually becomes a confirmed enthusiast, and on June 13, 1962 NASA test pilot Jack Reeder became the first foreign pilot to join that club. Reeder was an unusual test pilot in that he had never flown in the services, but he was vastly experienced. At the time of his visit to England, he had flown 177 different aircraft, including seven non-helicopter vertical takeoff and landing research craft. His experience of VTOL was unrivalled, so his opinion of the P1127 was eagerly awaited. He fell in love with it. Reeder had never flown an airplane with such a high thrust-to-weight ratio in conventional flight. In vertical takeoff he found it surprisingly easy to control—all fingers and wrist work, which made corrections very easy. He felt the designers had done an impressive job on improving the reaction controls, though the control in yaw clearly needed improving further.

One day, Reeder ran into Bill Bedford's bête noire — intake momentum drag yaw. He was burning off excess fuel on return from a sortie by lazily circling a castle near the end

of the runway. He was at about 150 feet, and he found himself making large corrections with his controls. He caught the
sideslip in time, opened the throttle, and banged the nozzles
aft to pick up airspeed. This was his only serious scare, and
he returned to America brimming over with enthusiasm for
the aircraft. The Vietnam war was building up at that time
and NASA was being asked for ideas in certain areas. Reeder
made out a case for buying the P1127 and developing its
limited capability for use in that war. His ideas were rejected,
but it is an intriguing hypothesis to conjecture what it might
have done in Southeast Asia.

Meanwhile, back in the corridors of power at the Ministry of Defense in London, the R.A.F. and the Royal Navy
were writing their requirements around the projected performance of the P1154. Already the seeds of its failure were being sown. The roles for which they were writing specifications
were almost diametrically opposed. The Royal Navy wanted
a two-seat, radar-equipped supersonic fighter with a primary
role of supersonic interception and a secondary role of low
altitude strike and close support. The Royal Air Force demand was for a single seat aircraft with a primary role of
close support and a secondary role of supersonic interception.
They could not have been much further apart. From the
start, the designers were being asked to squeeze too much
into one airframe. The truth is the Navy never wanted a
V/STOL airplane. What they had their eyes on was the Phantom which they would operate from the 50,000 ton carrier
for which the government had just given them permission.
The design office at Kingston on Thames spent 1962 and
most of 1963 trying in vain to reconcile the irreconcilable
between the two services. In the Ministry of Defense the
cyclic arguments went on literally day and night between
R.A.F. and Royal Navy, trying to agree on "commonality."
The Navy would not budge on its demands for two engines,
and there was much detailed argument over flight safety and

the load you could carry on an aircraft constrained by the power of a single engine as opposed to the twin-engine layout. The Navy maintained that the operation of vectored thrust off a ship's deck would pose insurmountable problems, but their strongest underlying motivation was that they saw jet V/STOL making a nonsense of their need for large, expensive conventional carriers. Bill Bedford's historic first carrier landing on February 8, 1963, could only have increased these fears, for it was an unqualified success.

Most of the south of England had been covered in deep snow for days, and they had to clear a patch of the runway at Dunsfold aerodrome to simulate the deck of a ship and get a bit of practice that way. The carrier *Ark Royal* was in Lyme Bay, just off Portland, and the exercise got off to rather a shaky start when the two Royal Navy Hunters escorting Bedford led him in to land on the wrong ship. It was reassuring to know that the Royal Navy is only human, and they quickly located the large bulk of the *Ark Royal*.

Bedford found that first vertical landing on a ship remarkably straightforward. There had been great concern in some people's minds that the abrupt change from free air to hovering over the deck would pose problems, but it was not so. He used the superstructure of the carrier's island as a very convenient height reference and put the prototype XP 831 smoothly down on the deck. He then did a series of vertical takeoffs and landings, short takeoffs, and lots of accelerating and decelerating transitions, one of which was at right angles across the deck. The nosewheel steering made taxiing easy within the confines of the deck, and though the wings did not fold, of course, the P1127 fitted easily into the lift and the hangar below decks. The crew was very worried about the effects of the hot jet efflux on the deck since the P1127 was not using a special platform. Immediately after every vertical lift-off, someone would rush over and place his hand tentatively on the deck. He found, as his confidence grew, that he

Chief Test Pilot Bill Bedford steps from the P1127 to be welcomed by the captain and crew of H.M.S. Ark Royal, *in Lyme Bay, February 1963. These were the first-ever jet V/STOL trials at sea.*

could leave his hand on the spot without any adverse effects. Bedford stayed on the carrier for several days and found the fixed wing Naval pilots absolutely fascinated by his aircraft. It was clear though that a large element also saw the concept as a serious threat to ships like the *Ark Royal*, which indeed, it was.

In the frustrating search for commonality, the Royal Navy demands were proving the more difficult to meet. Although the airframe makers were still in collaboration with the Bristol Aero Engine Company on the Pegasus, they found themselves working on a twin-engine Naval version of the P1154 with Rolls Royce at Derby. (The merger between the

two engine manufacturers didn't happen until the late 60's.)
It was an indication that Rolls Royce were conceding that
their multi-lift engine concept no longer had the rosy promise
it had once shown. The Rolls Royce engine proposed for this
variant was the Spey, then being used in the Buccaneer Navy
bomber and the Trident airliner. Rolls did some sums and calculated that two Speys, with plenum chamber burning,
would give enough thrust to lift the P1154 off a ship's deck.
The two engines were placed side by side with four nozzles,
and the two starboard nozzles were fed by one engine and
the port nozzles by the other.

Hawker was not bowled over by the two engine arguments. Two engines meant that if the pilot lost one "en
route," then the other would get him home, but the loss of
one on vertical takeoff would not leave him with enough
thrust to get up. And with two engines there was more than
twice as much chance of one engine failing! The other complication of the twin-engine layout was that if one failed, the
thrust would continue pouring out of the engine on the opposite side, and the aircraft would roll. They got around this
by crossing over the exhaust flows so that the port engine fed
the port front nozzles and the starboard rear one.

But it was a frustrating period for the design team,
because the impression was growing that the Navy did not
really want V/STOL anyway. They were hypnotized by the
McDonnell Douglas Phantom. By late 1963, the struggle for
"commonality" between the two services was no nearer reso-
lution. The Navy pulled out and went for a buy of Phantoms
from America.

There was an equally strong lobby within the R.A.F.
for Phantoms, instead of the P1154. The Phantom was a
proven, highly successful aircraft, not a "paper" airplane, and
supersonic or not, the V/STOL concept was still an unproven
operational concept. However, Britain was still a very significant world power, with commitments stretching East of

Suez, and she also had a large home aircraft industry to support. Buying dollar airplanes at the expense of the indigenous aircraft industry was not government policy, and so the R.A.F. told Hawker that their requirements still stood. They wanted supersonic performance from the P1154 not for their ground attack role but to help them escape heavily defended areas. The P1154 was designed to fly at 750 knots at tree top level. John Fozard, then Chief Designer of the aircraft, used to joke: "If you've used all your weapons, all you've got to do is bang the throttle through, and you'll burst the enemy's eardrums!"

Development of the P1154 was well under way when the new Labour government under Harold Wilson came to power. The new political leadership conducted a defense review which looked at the considerable range of ambitious technical developments on which both Navy and Air Force were embarked. Defense Minister Denis Healey decided that Britain could not sustain that level of investment in defense, and the axe came out. The overriding concern of the R.A.F. was that the TSR2 bomber should survive at any cost. Their secondary priority was the Armstrong Whitworth 681 V/STOL transport aircraft, and their lowest priority was the P1154. They argued that they could, if necessary, save money by taking the American Phantoms off the shelf and putting British engines in them. If the transport plane had to go, then they could buy the American Lockheed Hercules in its place. Whatever happened, they told Healey, the TSR2 must remain sacrosanct.

Healey listened carefully to this advice, then went ahead and scrapped TSR2, P1154 and the transport airplane. (He also cancelled the Navy's new carrier which seemed the death knell of fixed wing airpower at sea, until the Sea Harrier gave it back to them—via the concept they had been so skeptical about.) Healey told the R.A.F. that they would have the Hercules, a mix of Phantoms, and a developed version of the

Montage photograph of the cancelled supersonic V/STOL aircraft, the Hawker Siddeley P1154—seen here in its Royal Navy version.

P1127—the Harrier. The Air Force was not pleased. They had lost their cherished TSR2. They were to get Phantoms, which they admired, but they were also having foisted on them a subsonic V/STOL airplane in which they had never shown serious interest. What was more, the money they would have to spend on the Harriers to purchase sixty of them, initially, could be much better spent, they thought, on buying more Phantoms. In public, though, their stance was that this was the best of both worlds—Phantoms for Air Defense merging at the lower end of the spectrum with the quick response, ground attack Harriers.

The feelings at Kingston were a mixture of relief and regret. The subsonic aircraft, whose development had continued in low key throughout the P1154 saga, was finally to become a fully fledged production aircraft. If the subsonic airplane's development had not continued, then the cancellation of the P1154 would almost certainly have meant that Britain would have dropped out of vectored thrust V/STOL development there and then. However, the cancellation of the 1154 was not the only blow from the defense review for Hawker Siddeley. They were also the contractors for the V/STOL transport aircraft. The Hawker Siddeley management announced that the defense review would have to mean a loss of jobs, and they closed down an entire factory at Coventry. Ten thousand people lost their jobs, and there was a wave of political fury from the left wing who accused Hawker boss Sir Arnold Hall of firing workers in retaliation for government policies. John Fozard and colleague, Bob Marsh, who was then Chief Designer at Kingston, had the dreadful task of selecting people from the P1154 team to be let go. Some of them had been with the design team for a very long time. John Fozard recalled that he never felt so miserable in his life.

However, there was no question of the design effort from the P1154 project being thrown out. The first prototype was about one-third completed, and a total of around three-quarters of a million engineering man hours had gone into it. Much of it was to be directly applicable to the aircraft later to become the Harrier, and this included the navigation and attack system. Throughout the political/military hassle surrounding the supersonic aircraft, the P1127 was taken a step further and turned into the Kestrel. Nine of these airplanes were taking part in a unique international collaboration designed to assess the practicality of V/STOL operations in the field.

The lesson of the tripartite squadron, combined with the technical advances of the P1154, produced the Harrier which was to start squadron service with the R.A.F. in 1969.

The majority of the Air Staff may have been dismayed by the government decision to impose this subsonic "jump jet" on them. However, the handful of junior officers who had the opportunity to fly it and see it in action from rough, dispersed sites, had no such doubts. A nucleus of pilots, fired with enthusiasm, was already growing for the exciting new concept.

Since 1962 work had been going on towards developing the P1127 into the Kestrel for the tripartite squadron flying. At the Paris Air Show, in June 1963, the prototype XP 831 crashed in the most humiliating circumstances as the representatives of the governments sponsoring the prospective squadron, 150,000 spectators and television viewers around the world watched. It was a public relations man's nightmare. There was not only the tripartite squadron to think of. The P1154 was still going strong, and the vectored thrust principle was on show to prospective future purchasers of the supersonic version too. The P1127 was given the brief of dazzling them all with the basic simplicity of the British concept.

It got off to a bad start when one of the two prototypes had starting problems, but by late afternoon, on Sunday, June 16, 1963, both aircraft were fully serviceable. At 5:13 they lifted off for their demonstration. The French Balzac had already given its demonstration to the chauvinistically enthusiastic French crowd. Its rather cumbersome transitions were cleverly hidden by having conventional Mirage jet fighters screaming around at the same time, and giving the impression that they had an all speed airplane in the Balzac. This, of course, was not true. It took off from a gridded platform, hidden neatly by rising ground!

The two British aircraft gave a most impressive display which had the French crowd enthused, and Bedford in XP 831 came in for a vertical landing. The Balzac had been forced to land on a large concrete platform next to the President's marquee. As a piece of one-upmanship Bedford intended to show that the British aircraft could land quite happily on the grass next to the platform. All eyes were on the P1127. Without warning, and within a fraction of a second, the nozzles suddenly swung from the vertical back towards the horizontal. The aircraft immediately lost its jet lift and dropped spectacularly right on top of the concrete platform. Bedford braced himself for the impact but surprisingly was unhurt. As the aircraft crumpled on to the concrete he saw smoke, dust and lots of aircraft pieces flying all over the place. A wheel bounced at speed into the middle distance. He cut the high pressure fuel cock, shutting down the engine, and stepped out in a daze. Hawker Siddeley director Bob Lickley was fighting a vain battle to keep photographers at bay, but the French press were intent on a field day. Bedford and the others were stricken, and one newspaper summed the crash up by saying, "It was a thud that was heard all round the world." What had caused it?

The culprit was a little piece of grit, which had jammed the pressure-reducing valve protecting the air motors driving the nozzles from too much high pressure air. The aircraft was already in a nose-down hovering position when the jamming took place, and when the nozzles swivelled backwards, the downwards plunge was inevitable.

The prestige of the aircraft company and the country had taken a severe knock. In real terms, though, it was the sort of fluke accident which eventually left little bad impression on the technically knowledgeable.

Chapter 6

The Tripartite Squadron

The tripartite evaluation squadron was the brainchild of an American businessman, Larry Levy. He made his fortune from aviation accessories and in 1961, was one of those "dollar a year" men encouraged by the late President Kennedy to go out into the world and take time out from their own interests, to further America's. He spent a year in the MWDP office in Paris where, as we know, V/STOL was an everyday topic of conversation. There were, of course, many attempts made in America to come up with a viable V/STOL aircraft, but Britain's P1127 was the only one anything like an operational aircraft. Levy conceived the idea of getting something positive for the money MWDP had already spent on the P1127, by testing the concept in the field with an international squadron.

Britain had already withdrawn her operational requirement for the P1127, but Levy managed to persuade them that it was in their interests to keep the P1127 project alive. So, throughout the P1154 saga, Britain did in fact hedge her

A Kestrel of the Tripartite Evaluation Squadron in the international squadron's distinctive markings.

bets by keeping the subsonic aircraft in continuous development and at the same time, gaining valuable lessons which would be applied to the P1154 when it eventually entered service. With hindsight, it was a very wise decision. The United States and Great Britain provided about 12.8 million pounds each, and the Federal Republic of Germany about a million pounds less.

There were to be nine P1127's in the tripartite trials, and from the time of the signing of the agreement in late 1961, development work was directed at turning the prototypes into what would be the Kestrel. The planning team for the squadron was set up in January 1964, and training commenced at the end of that year. The Squadron Commander was Wing Commander David Scrimgeour of the Royal Air Force. He was thirty-eight years old and had wide jet fighter experience, including a two-year exchange with the United States Air Force. The two Deputy Commanders were Commander J. J. Tyson of the U.S. Navy and Colonel Gerhard Barkhorn of the German Air Force. Although Barkhorn was in his mid-forties and the oldest pilot by a number of years, no one doubted his ability to handle himself. He was the world's second top-scoring fighter pilot with over 300 victories, mostly on the Russian front.

The other pilots in the ten-man squadron were three from the Royal Air Force, a young colleague of Colonel Barkhorn's from the Luftwaffe, and three other American pilots. Of the Americans two were from the Army and one, Colonel 'J. K.' Campbell, from the U.S.A.F. Interestingly, the U.S. Marine Corps, which only four years later was to buy the Harrier, was not even represented though they did follow the reports from their "big brother" the U.S. Navy.

The German participation in the tripartite squadron had been stimulated by their own involvement in V/STOL aircraft development. Since 1961, they had been working, amongst other projects, on the VAK 191, a tactical close support fighter. The initials of the name stood for Vertical Startendes Augklarungs-und-Kampflugzeug (vertical takeoff and landing fighter aircraft). The VAK 191, however, had not yet flown, and in fact, it did not make its first flight until 1971. The squadron's flying was seen as an excellent testing ground for pilot experience in the new concept. The VAK 191 had two Rolls Royce lift engines wedded to a sort of half-scale Pegasus with four nozzles sited in the middle of the fuselage. It had tiny wings and very limited maneuverability, lacking the British aircraft's ability to use excess thrust for maneuvering at low level. For a straight line, low level mission the VAK 191 design was fine, and attractive though it may have been for the Germans to consider adopting the single-engine British vectored thrust concept, it wasn't politically acceptable in Germany to make a carbon copy P1127.

It is interesting though that just as the tripartite squadron was forming, the United States Air Force was attracted enough by the VAK 191 project to put some money into its avionics development. Eventually this brave effort by the new post-war German aircraft industry went the way of every other Western competitor to the simple, effective British answer to V/STOL, and was scrapped in the early 70's. As we will see later this was certainly mourned more by the manufacturers than by the senior echelons of the German Air Force.

The U.S. Army had been playing the leading role in generating interest in V/STOL in America at that time, for a very good reason. They were just entering a major battle with the U.S. Air Force for control of tactical airpower. Their argument was that they were the infantry in the slit trenches, therefore they ought to control their own airpower. They wanted to take the relevant aircraft right out of the Air Force inventory. Eventually, of course, the battle was resolved, at the highest level, by the dictum that the Army could operate armed helicopters or gunships for close support, and the Air Force would have command and control of the tactical, conventional fixed wing airplanes. At the time of the tripartite evaluation this was not resolved, and in the Kestrel, the U.S. Army saw a very capable, close support aircraft which could be operated by their own pilots in support of their own troops.

Their difficulty was that when the squadron was being formed, all their pilots' experience was either on helicopters or fixed wing light aircraft. So, the initial part of the squadron training was directed towards putting that right. All ten squadron pilots, in fact, did about ten hours on Hunter jets and then about five hours on helicopters. The U.S. Army people were vastly experienced in helicopters, but it gave the other pilots a chance to judge what it was like sitting stationary fifty feet up. Then it was off to the Hawker Siddeley airfield at Dunsfold for conversion to the Kestrel.

Everyone was agreeably surprised, not to say relieved, that it went so smoothly. No one had any particular problems and most of the pilots commented on how natural it seemed to make the transitions from hover to wingborne flight. They started off with one conventional flight and then went straight into vertical takeoffs and landings. There were, of course, no two-seat aircraft then, though there was one occasion on which the watchers on the ground wished fervently there had been. This was the incident which became known as the "Barkhorn Turn."

Gerhard Barkhorn, the fighter ace, was a superb natural pilot but some of his colleagues felt that in his flying career he must have had his share of luck, for he seemed to get away with the most amazing things. He had lifted off vertically from the grid at Dunsfold and intended to hold it at fifty feet in the hover, but found it wandering over the edge of the grid. The intake momentum drag yaw phenomenon did not mean as much to the daring German as it did to people like Bill Bedford watching on the ground. They winced as Barkhorn performed a small and very hesitant circle to get himself back over the grid. Needless to say, he managed it without a hint of sideslip developing.

With conversion completed, the squadron which included ground crews from the three nations, made their way to R.A.F. West Raynham for the squadron's official formation on April 1, 1965.

Several important design changes had been made to the 1127 to turn it into the Kestrel. One of the most obvious differences was the change from the straight across forty-five degrees delta wing to a proper swept wing. The outrigger wheels remained at the wing tips but the original wing tip design had been causing pitching difficulties, and a tendency for the wing to drop. The outrigger legs were now housed in a pod at the wing tip which gave a more aesthetic and efficient curved tip. The wing also now used a different form of con-

Some of the pilots of the Tripartite Evaluation Squadron. Back row (left to right)—Squadron Leader Fred Trowern, R.A.F.; Lt. Col. Lou Solt, U.S. Army; Wing Commander David McL. Scrimgeour, R.A.F. (Commanding Officer); Col. Gerhard Barkhorn, Luftwaffe; Flt. Lt. David Edmonston, R.A.F. Front row (left to right)—Captain V. Suhr, Luftwaffe; Major Al Johnson, U.S. Army; Lt. Col. J. K. Campbell, U.S. Air Force; Lt. Cdr. J. J. Tyson, U.S. Navy; Flt. Lt. "Porky" Munro, R.A.F.

struction—integral machined skins as opposed to the more vulnerable spot welded surfaces. It also carried more fuel than the 1127 wing, and although the earlier wing had never leaked, it was not considered worth the risk continuing with the spot welded construction. Prototypes, after all, do not fly long enough for serious fatigue problems to show up.

There were also problems of longitudinal control in con-

ventional flight, and these were eased by a new anhedral or
drooped tailplane, and an inertia weight in the control circuit.
The ever present problem of center of gravity was tackled
again by stretching the fuselage of the Kestrel and taking the
wing with it. The reaction controls were also improved. The
puffers on the wing tips were now provided with valves which
blew up as well as down. This last improvement was considered vital by the test pilots who had been carrying out the
development flying. They were running into difficulties of
intake momentum drag yaw at speeds up to one hundred
knots and were adamant that the roll control power could
and should be doubled by this modification. In fact, many of
the improvements had been achieved only after an intense
internal struggle which no one outside the program knew
about at the time.

The basic dichotomy which has to be resolved internally
in an aircraft development program like the P1127, is this:
does one insist on a perfect prototype which arrives too late
and is too expensive? Or does one churn it out so that it
reaches service at an unacceptably low standard? Eventually a
crunch point is reached where designers, test pilots and company managers have to sit round a table and reach the compromise which means the right airplane at the right price, at
the right time. The test pilots, led by Bill Bedford, wanted to
finish up with a typical, classic Hawker aircraft with good
handling qualities, stability and control, and a minimum of
limitations. Their principal concern was that the German and
American pilots would not return home soured about the
V/STOL concept because of basic bad handling qualities.
Hawker management was interested in getting the airplane
into squadron service with minimum delay, and they vigorously challenged the need for several of the fundamental
changes the pilots were asking for. A lot of tact and ingenuity
was needed to change their minds.

Bedford and Merewether had several long "pilot sessions" with Wing Commander Scrimgeour, Squadron Leader J. Henderson, Colonel Barkhorn, Commander Tyson and NASA test pilot Jack Reeder, several of whom sat in on management board discussions concerning the Kestrel. This unofficial test pilots' union made an unwritten agreement to "fight like hell" for the changes. They must have argued convincingly.

R. A. F. West Raynham in Norfolk on the east coast of England was a fighter station with two operational squadrons of Hunters. It was an ideal base from which the tripartite squadron could operate. There was a large grass airfield nearby at Bircham Newton, and a few miles off was the British Army's battle training area which included about forty square miles of government-controlled countryside, which was ideal for practicing dispersed site operation. Two Hunters were detached for the squadron's use in continuation training, and they also had a U.S. Army Iroquois helicopter which was to prove invaluable for transporting equipment in the field.

The V/STOL concept was very much on trial with the eyes of the military of three countries firmly fixed on the squadron's progress. It was a great pity it got off to such a poor start. On almost the first day, a U.S. Army pilot crashed one of the nine precious aircraft. He was attempting a short takeoff and forgot to release the parking brake. He lined up, opened the throttle and, of course, the brakes could not hold the aircraft back. It skidded on full power and both the main wheels blew. The P1127 cartwheeled and caught fire. The pilot had about 6,000 hours on helicopters, but no fixed wing jet experience apart from the ten hours' Hunter conversion course. He was discreetly withdrawn from the program and replaced with another Army pilot, but there was a lot of sympathy for the grounded man. It was not a mistake he was ever likely to repeat, and if there had not been so much at stake, he might have been allowed to carry on. Shortly after that, another pilot did a vertical takeoff with the parking brake on but he got away with it because he landed vertically too. This cannot happen on the present aircraft because the opening of the throttle automatically releases the parking brake.

During the squadron's nine months of operational flying, the eight remaining aircraft flew almost a thousand sorties, totalling around 650 flying hours. They operated mostly away from their main base at West Raynham flying from a wide variety of sites in woods, grass airfields and ordinary farm fields. One of the objects of the exercise was to measure takeoff and landing distances from these unprepared sites and to determine the surfaces from which one could operate safely. They developed techniques of testing the hardness of the ground by plunging in a device called a "cone penetrometer." They discovered that if you could drive over a field in a jeep and found the undulations acceptable, then you could probably do a short takeoff from it in a Kestrel. They landed and took off continuously from the same fields and clearings, and measured how long it took before the grass showed damage and scorching which would betray the position from the air. It was a thrilling sight to watch the Kestrels rising straight out of the waist-height grass at Bircham Newton.

Bill Bedford and other test pilots were on call to assist in solving any problems which cropped up in the field. He flew some sorties at West Raynham in a P1127 in the squadron's earliest days when snow was on the ground. It was an ideal opportunity, with snow being swirled around by the jet efflux, to try to find out the minimum speeds at which you should fly forward to prevent foreign objects like stones being sucked into the engine. Operating from rough surfaces this could have been a serious problem. However, with just a bit of forward speed, nose and engine intakes stayed clear of the snow cloud. It showed that on bad surfaces, "rolling landings" at around forty knots would minimize the foreign object damage.

The fourth phase of the exercise got down to the nuts and bolts of assessing the airplane in the role for which it had been designed—operation from dispersed sites. They assumed that the squadron was based at a primary site, which in some instances was a rough field. Around the primary site at distances between five and twenty miles were a number of so-called sub-sites which were stocked with different levels of support, from full fuel and rearming facilities down to no logistics support at all. They were attempting to establish just how much back up the aircraft would need under operational conditions. Although the aircraft had a rudimentary gunsight, they were not actually carrying any weapons. They based their calculations on the amount of weapons the aircraft would need based on the sort of turn-around they were achieving between sorties.

The primary site was the squadron headquarters with full refuelling and rearming facilities, full ground crews and a complete operations control center. In one mode of operation, a pilot took off from the primary site, fully fuelled and "armed" and landed vertically on a sub-site just behind the main "battle area." He waited there until he was called in on a ground attack mission. Sub-sites like these required little or no facilities. Others they experimented with had varying degrees of logistics support. The greater the permutations, the more they were learning.

By pure coincidence, the life of the tripartite squadron ran parallel with the end of the P1154 project and the decision to order a developed version of the Kestrel for squadron service with the Royal Air Force. The company gave the new aircraft the name P1127 (R.A.F.). It was not christened Harrier until 1967. All the lessons being learned by Wing Commander Scrimgeour and his squadron during those months were fed straight back to the R.A.F. Operational Requirements Office at the Ministry of Defense. This feedback resulted in the operational requirement being written in a remarkably short time.

*The first Kestrel, XS688, in Tripartite Squadron markings,
in formation with a two-seat Hawker Hunter, 1964.*

The Kestrel used the Pegasus 5 engine rated at 15,000 pounds thrust. Considering that it was a new engine and completely new aircraft, combined with the additional problems of servicing in the field, the squadron managed to maintain a creditable 50 per cent serviceability. They may not have been firing bombs and rockets, but the international ground crews were turning those aircraft around in the conditions that the R.A.F. envisaged their new aircraft being operated. The lessons that the manufacturers learned about maintenance were invaluable. For example, the squadron's ground crews grumbled about the lack of accessibility. They were having to crawl up in a hole under the fuselage behind the engine, to get at equipment in the rear fuselage. The designers knew from the operational requirement that the Harrier was going to carry much more in the way of avionics. So they cut two holes in the rear fuselage, mounted the gear on shelves and now the engineers stand and work at normal height.

The squadron was finding that short takeoffs from grass presented no problems, but they were also experimenting with artificial surfaces for vertical takeoff and landing pads. Apart from interlocking metal sheets, they also tried an extraordinary mixture of polyester resin and glass fiber. This was sprayed on the ground and within a few hours hardened completely and stood up extremely well. In fact, the U.S. Marines still use it for this purpose today. It can be camouflage painted now, but in those early trials it was a somewhat inappropriate blush pink color. They worked normally with a pad about seventy-five feet square and got it down to about twenty-five feet, but they found this too small for operational use.

Throughout the trials, everyone kept their fingers crossed that no one would have to do a vertical landing miles away from base through lack of fuel. The thrust over weight margin was so small that they were still very limited in the amount of fuel they could carry. This never happened, but the high speed guardian angel who watched over Gerhard Barkhorn finally took a day off. He shut the throttle prematurely during a slow landing and destroyed most of the undercarriage. Then he completely disarmed everyone by stepping from the aircraft and announcing, "Completely my fault; nothing to do with the airplane at all." It could, of course, have simply been that a subtle form of attack was the best type of self-defense. He did not shoot down 300 airplanes without learning something!

At one stage, the squadron gave a demonstration to senior officers and leading figures from the aircraft industry, in the Stamford battle training area. Sir Sydney Camm was there, showing as always an intense interest in the detailed design of his aircraft. After the demonstration was over, the aircraft were parked, and the crowd was relaxing, except Sir

ʿSydney. John Dale was strolling along the line of aircraft when he saw a figure crouched under the rear fuselage of one. There had clearly been disagreements back at Kingston over the "pen nib" fairings under the hot nozzles which protected the airframe from the exhaust. Sir Sydney beckoned Dale and snorted, "Would you look at that for a piece of design!"

At the end of the nine months' intensive flying, the squadron had proved that the Kestrel could operate away from main bases at sites with and without logistical support. They also proved something else, by dispelling the myth that it took a super-pilot to handle the vectored thrust airplane. Of course, it would "bite" you if you didn't follow the rules, but average operational pilots on the squadron had coped. This was most encouraging for the aircraft's entry into R. A. F. service.

The unit as a whole wrote and submitted an official report which said, in essence, that the dispersed operation was a viable concept, although they were not able at that stage to assess accurately the cost. The squadron pilots had been unequivocally enthusiastic about the Kestrel, and both the German and the American teams went on to write individual reports for their own services. The reports were known to be glowing, even though they were never published. Yet, no further collaboration on the aircraft ensued from this highly successful experiment in international cooperation, and there were no sales of the British aircraft to either of the two countries. It was to be three years before the United States Marine Corps decided unilaterally to go for the Harrier.

The Americans took back with them to the States their three Kestrels and also, with the permission of the Federal Republic of Germany, the three German planes. In America, the aircraft carried out a series of tri-service trials for the Army, Navy and Air Force including some of the earliest shipboard operations. Several were cannibalized for spares, but one which went to NASA, Langley, went on to contribute some vitally important research flying on the combat maneuvering program. This aircraft is now in the Smithsonian Institution in Washington. However, back in 1966, after these tri-service trials, no further interest was shown in the aircraft. At that time, in terms of payload, the V/STOL concept seemed too high a penalty to pay. The Navy at that time saw no reason to doubt the efficacy of their large carriers, the Air Force could see little sense in dispersing away from main runways in the United States, and of course the Army was getting out of fixed wing flying anyway.

In Germany, the aftermath of the tripartite squadron was more complex. The government was backing the aircraft industry in its attempts to produce a homegrown V/STOL fighter in the form of the VAK 191, but the attitude of the Luftwaffe was very different. They were thoroughly disenchanted by the technical advice they had following the Lockheed F104 Starfighter. It was an interceptor that they had to turn into a low level aircraft with a lot of extra weight, complexity of weapons and a resultant bad accident record. And now V/STOL. The unofficial Air Force line was that V/STOL was bad news. It was the unknown, and they believed they should be going for something more conventional, something they could understand. The outcome was that the Kestrel evaluation pilots were ordered by their chiefs back in Germany not to enthuse about it, for fear of encouraging the concept generally.

In retrospect, it would have been naive to have expected anything more concrete to come from an international collaboration of something so politically involved as airplanes. However, Britain was now reaping the benefits of her involvement in the squadron.

Chapter 7

Development Problems: Spinning and Side-Slip

In the four years between the Kestrel squadron and the entry of the Harrier into R.A.F. service, the airplane underwent great changes. To the casual observer it may have looked pretty much the same as the Kestrel, but it was in fact a 90 per cent redesign. The test pilots were now embarking on some of the highest risk test flying of the whole program. This was a period which was to bring several of them very close to death. In the unemotional language of test pilots, the word "professionalism" tends to be substituted for courage, when they are describing their own or their colleagues' experiences. A layman need feel no such constraint. They are brave men.

The Harrier, like all fighters, had to go through an academic spinning program to meet a Ministry of Defense requirement that it spin for up to four turns and then recover. Fighters in combat are not going to be deliberately spun, but in the heat of battle it can happen accidentally. Aircraft are flown to the limits of their maneuverability to try to catch or

escape from another one, and pilots may occasionally go outside the limits and spin. The interest in the spinning trials was
not the entry to the spin, but the recovery which involves the
best way to move the stick, ailerons and rudder bar, flaps, airbrakes and anything else the pilot has control over. Now, to
investigate this one wants a nice, repeatable spin so that the
"trace" recorder in the airplane demonstrates, in analysis back
on the ground, the differences in various recovery techniques.
Hugh Merewether, who was flying those trials, found he just
could not get the Harrier to spin repeatedly. He took the
most "pro-spin" condition which is straight and level flight
very close to the point of stall. He then closed the throttle,
pulled back hard on the stick and kicked on full rudder—the
sort of thing all trainee pilots have to do to induce a practice
spin. Sometimes, it would not spin at all, and at other times,
it would spin for one or two turns then, even with the controls held in a pro-spinning position, the Harrier would break
out of its own accord.

Now, from the point of view of an academic spinning
trial this was bad news, but from the designer and operational
pilot point of view it was delightful, because it meant that
the airplane was very unlikely to spin in service. (What a con-
fidence-builder for a fighter pilot.) But, Hugh Merewether
and the rest of the development team realized that in service
even the most spin-reluctant aircraft would be accidentally
spun. Some freak combination of circumstances (loading,
wind gusts, rate of turn, aircraft attitude, fuel state) could
mean that the operational pilot might get into a situation
which the test pilot had not produced, and the plane would
spin.

Hugh Merewether thought long and hard about the
problem and concluded that the engine was the principal factor. They'd gone to a lot of trouble, of course, to "contra-
rotate" the engine for the very reason that when the aircraft
was suddenly disturbed, the power plant should not make it

move in some other way by gyroscopic forces. Hugh reasoned that when he tried to spin the Harrier, he did not have the help that a normal engine might have given him, because normal engines did not have this steadying influence. So, why not try it with the engine stopped?

On his next sortie, at 35,000 feet, he stopped the engine. He waited about half a minute until the Pegasus had slowed down to the condition where the blades were just windmilling, then tried to spin. The Harrier went immediately into a nice, repeatable spin. What he did, though, was a carefully calculated but rather dramatic action. He stopped the aircraft's only engine, deliberately put the aircraft out of control, and spun it down to 10,000 feet. Then, when the whole trial should have been over, he had to set about restarting the engine. It was characteristic of the rather introverted Merewether that he got on with the job and did not tell many people about how he was achieving his results. He just went out over the English Channel and did it. Unfortunately, on one sortie, his luck almost ran out. It was to be the last spin of the entire program.

Merewether shut the engine down as usual at altitude and entered the spin. At around 10,000 feet he started his recovery actions. Nothing happened. The next step in the standard procedure was to stream the anti-spin parachute to try to lift the tail and point the airplane straight down, building up speed in a dive, as opposed to fluttering down in the spin. Far below, the whitecaps of the Channel waves and the dark shapes of the merchant ships tumbled in and out of vision in a steady 360 degrees sweep as the Harrier spiralled relentlessly towards the sea. At 8,000 feet, the point of no return if he were ever going to bring it back under control, the Harrier responded to his straining foot on the opposite rudder. He pulled it out of the dive, re-lit the engine and went home. If the Harrier had not recovered there and then, he would have had to eject.

The analysis of the traces back at Dunsfold showed why he had such difficulty in controlling the aircraft. The traces showed that he was only a few seconds away from losing all his flying controls. They are power operated by the hydraulic system and if the engine stops, the hydraulics also stop. The engine had slowed right down to below normal windmilling speed in the spin, so he lost his hydraulic pressure. The controls had only been a few pounds per square inch above the point of locking solid, when the Harrier recovered from the spin. It was hardly surprising that the test pilot had such a struggle. The Ministry wisely decided that the spinning program should end there. They were satisfied that the aircraft was "most reluctant to spin," and that the main recovery techniques had been established.

The Harrier has not been spun deliberately since, and it is a tribute to the design that not a single aircraft has been lost in service through spinning. That is probably unique amongst fighters, and it is one of the strongest compliments the Americans pay it. A Harrier pilot knows that if he loses control and spins, he can regain control just by relaxing. It remains to be seen whether the advanced Harrier, the AV-8B, with its bigger wing will spin as well as the Harrier. If it does not, then the combat pilot will have to back off before he reaches the limit, thus reducing his maneuverability advantage. Test pilots like Merewether took a calculated professional risk and got away with it. There was, however, one characteristic of the airplane at that time which lurked, waiting to punish any pilot who grew unwary.

The first pilot to die in a Harrier crash was Major Chuck Rosburgh of the United States Air Force. He was the victim of intake momentum drag yaw, the same phenomenon which Bill Bedford had encountered from the earliest days. His death, however, was the spur which led Hawker Siddeley to tackle what was then a dangerous characteristic of the airplane. Chuck Rosburgh died on his final sortie in 1969 before returning to America after a successful tour of duty evaluating the Harrier. He was a very competent pilot, and no novice on V/STOL. He'd flown the Kestrel in the United States before coming to England, so he knew well the dangers of allowing the airplane to point anywhere except the direction it was going, at speeds in excess of fifty knots. At low speeds, it doesn't have to point its nose where it's going. It can go backwards or sideways quite safely. But, as we discussed earlier, at slightly higher speeds, before the fin of the airplane has sufficient airflow over it to control the airplane's direction, it is directionally very unstable. The air rushing into the Pegasus intakes, ahead of the center of gravity, makes the nose want to swing round. The intakes are fighting the fin until the fin gets more powerful as speed increases. So, between 50 and 110 knots, the amount of safe sideways movement is small.

Major Rosburgh's last sortie was from the woods at Dunsfold Airfield. He lifted off vertically and started accelerating into the transition, when the aircraft started to sideslip. It seemed he put on some rudder to prevent flying over a parked fire engine. The fatal sequence had started. An uncontrollable roll started to develop, and the Major either applied the wrong rudder to correct, or decided simply that the situation was beyond his control. We will never know. There was almost ninety degrees of bank on the wings when he pulled the ejection handle. He blasted out of the cockpit sideways, and the rocket seat slammed him straight into the runway. The Harrier itself slid into the ground a short distance away. It was horrifying to see a man die that way. Up until that day the pilots who flew the airplane had somehow failed to impress the people with the money just how serious the problem was. Chuck Rosburgh's death had been captured at twenty-four chilling frames per second by a movie cameraman. The company chiefs needed no further convincing that something must be done, and development money was provided.

All that Chuck Rosburgh had, to tell him of sideways movement, was a simple little wind vane on a post outside the windscreen. If the vane was pointing roughly ahead then the pilot knew the Harrier was going through the sky that way. If it was pointing off to right or left it indicated how much sideways movement he had. If the nozzles were pushed forward into the braking stop and the Harrier was flying backwards, then the vane would be pointing straight at him. Although the vane would tell the pilot that he was going sideways at ninety degrees, it did not tell him whether it was safe or not to do that. Airspeed was the critical factor, and the pilot only got that by looking at his airspeed indicator. Pilots like John Farley had long said that it was only a matter of time before someone failed to realize quickly enough that his airspeed was too high for the position of his wind vane. The unfortunate Major Rosburgh had proved the truth of that prediction.

The attack on the problem was three-pronged. The first development was a side-force indicator, a genuine, purpose-built Harrier instrument which is now incorporated on the head-up display. This is a marker which has to be kept roughly centered at all times, and if this is done it will not allow the pilot to fly the aircraft sideways at too high a speed. It is a very effective device, but still an instrument and something that the pilot has to look at.

The next step was to incorporate an attention-getting warning device. Flashing lights were discounted because of problems in daylight and in situations like hovering where the pilot was looking outside the cockpit a lot. They settled on a tactile warning system or something that would shake the rudder when sideforce got to a dangerous level. This would alert the pilot to danger and also remind him that he has to sort out the problem with his feet. It would go further, and shake the rudder pedal that he would have to push to make the correction, without resort to looking at an instrument at all. The pedal shaker was operated by another simple accelerometer, mounted on the bulkhead behind the pilot's seat, which measures sideways acceleration. The warning comes up at a very low level of G, just .06. When one considers that one tenth of a G does not feel like much at all, then .06 might seem negligible. That's the whole point, though, because that amount of almost imperceptible sideways force is enough potentially to start upsetting the aircraft's control.

Having sorted out that area, they then concentrated on a way of trying to make the Harrier not want to go sideways in the first place. As we have seen, the conflict between the Pegasus intakes and the aircraft's fin produces directional instability up to around 110 knots. During that time, until the fin takes over, the pilot is working the yaw puffers with his feet on the rudder bar. They decided to put in a system which would operate the yaw puffers automatically if the airplane started to go sideways. They put in another lateral accelerometer which fed a signal to an autostabilizer which "told" the puffer to open and pull the nose around one way or the other. It does raise the question of why did they not do this right at the beginning? The problem they faced was the possibility of failure. It took quite a lot of control authority away from the pilot if it was to work successfully, and all electrical systems malfunction sooner or later. The autostabilizer could well make the airplane go sideways at a time when the pilot did not want it to. It was a trade-off between whether an automatic gimmick was likely to prevent more accidents than it caused. After the Rosburgh accident, the balance of opinion was very much in favor of autostabilization, but because of its inherent dangers, a lot of test flying had to be done which looked quite deliberately at possible failures. John Farley described it laconically as, "one of the higher risk test flight problems." His colleagues have described it as some of the most courageous flying they have ever seen.

Autostabilizer failure tests as such are fairly routine.

This one, though, was different in that the yaw autostabilizer was there essentially to protect the airplane taking off and landing, so the failures had to be simulated very close to the ground. The extremely low altitude was important also because altitudes high enough to reduce the risk could have affected engine thrust and distort the conclusions. So, day after day, Farley took off at Dunsfold and flew across the airfield at about one hundred feet at speeds between fifty and one hundred knots. There was a switch in the cockpit which caused the autostabilization to malfunction. He threw the switch and waited. There was a deliberate delay of up to eight seconds which was intended to catch the pilot slightly unawares, thus simulating as near as possible a genuine failure in service. Suddenly, the system would bang in half yaw puffer, and the Harrier would start to yaw and then roll. The test was to see how quickly Farley could catch it with corrective action. He did this again and again, flying slower and slower, and allowing the yaw and the subsequent roll to get worse and worse before he caught it. All this, so close to the ground that there was scarcely any margin for error. Later, he built in his own artificial delay of a second or so after the failure to simulate the actions of a service pilot caught so much by surprise that he reacted slowly.

It was the same with the pedal shakers. Farley had to demonstrate that the shakers would go off in time to save the airplane if the pilot reacted properly. They built in the delay again. He would sit on final approach at around 200 feet, and throw the failure switch. Around would come the nose, he let the aircraft yaw, and then he let it start to roll. He had to resist the temptation to touch the rudder. When the pedal shaker started, he waited half a second and then hit that pedal. He finished off the program by taking the Harrier up to 2,000 feet and flying it hands off at around fifty knots, kicking on full rudder and letting the airplane right itself without any corrective action from the pilot. In the end, the system was really that good. More than that no one could ask. It was eighteen months since the fatal crash at Dunsfold. Chuck Rosburgh's death had not been totally futile. The changes it brought about were a direct consequence of his fatal crash. However, outside this emotive atmosphere, development continued of other aspects of the airplane's performance.

The Harrier shape, as we have seen before, was dictated by the Pegasus engine anyway, and this was again increased to 19,000 pounds thrust by getting more air through and burning more fuel in it. The intake was changed in size and given sixteen auxiliary doors to improve airflow into the engine, and a new low authority pitch and roll autostabilizer was developed to aid control in the V/STOL modes. It was clear that with the stores the Harrier was going to carry under its wings, something would have to be done yet again to get the center of gravity right. It was moved further forward.

The self-starter, an important development for an aircraft operating frequently away from support facilities, was built in. The Harrier also had the benefit of a much improved undercarriage. The nosewheel steering was improved, and the nosewheel tire changed to help its flotation on boggy ground. But, the most important undercarriage change was the design of a two stage oleo for the main leg. This meant that at all weights the aircraft's ground handling was vastly better because the aircraft rested more securely on the outriggers until lift-off.

However, the most fundamental change was to turn the Kestrel from a flying machine into a fighting machine — a weapons system. The Ferranti inertial navigation system and the Smiths' head-up display, which we have already looked at, was the basis of this and had in fact been designed for the ill-fated P1154. The accuracy of this system required to be tested by many hours of flying. They painted a cross on the airfield and pinpointed its latitude and longitude. They

Rocket pods being fitted during turnaround between sorties to an R.A.F. Harrier GR1 of No. 4 Squadron in a hide in West Germany.

then went off and flew for an hour and a half and taxied back over exactly the same spot. The computer on board the aircraft, driving the navigation system, though, might well say that the aircraft was half a mile away from that spot. However, nothing is that simple. The designers would then say, "Ah, but do you think it was perhaps three-quarters of a mile out after half an hour? Did all the error develop early in the flight while the equipment was cool or did it happen as it got hot?"

John Farley who was doing much of the test flying at that time would take off and fly a predetermined route crossing over obvious landmarks. He took a picture of each landmark which showed the aircraft's exact position in relation to it. These photographed positions were then transferred onto the stored map positions which the computer had been feeding in. The difference between the two was the navigational error. This was all very tedious from the test flying point of view, but the importance was fundamental. They also had to find out how the nav/attack system fared when put through high stress maneuvers like aerobatics.

They carried a wide range of underwing stores to discover if they affected the aircraft handling. Rockets were fired from all the pylons on the airframe at different speeds and heights. There were also the more mundane but equally important new aspects of the operational aircraft which had to be made to work. Did the flight-refuelling probe splash fuel into the engine intakes? What would happen when they jettisoned fuel? They found the answer to the latter by painting whitewash all over the back of the aircraft then jettisoning fuel in flight. The whitewash showed clearly whether fuel vapor or droplets were likely to be sucked back into the airplane. There were also special bolt-on wing tips to be tested and proven. These would spread the weight of the aircraft over a larger area of sky, thus increasing the ferry range at altitude by about nine per cent, compared with the normal combat wing. Unlike an ordinary military aircraft where all these aspects are embodied in the early development, this work could not start until after the Kestrel phase had proved the other, unique features of the airplane.

The aircraft also had to go on tropical and arctic trials, since it was likely to be operated in both extremes of temperature. How would it perform when it was covered in snow, or surrounded by sand in a temperature when the airframe was too hot to touch? In snow, they discovered that they could not do vertical takeoffs because of the blinding blizzard blown up by the exhaust from the downward pointing nozzles. Their solution was to park on the takeoff pad with nozzles down and open the throttle slightly. In a very short time, the snow had melted, and they were sitting on a patch of dry, clean ground. Then they let the snow and general dust settle around before lifting off. Whatever its fighting qualities, the Harrier was clearly going to be a great runway clearance vehicle!

The same technique could be used for vertical landings, by keeping enough fuel in hand to hover for a few minutes above the landing spot to clear it. For slow, or so-called rolling vertical landings, Farley discovered, as Bill Bedford had done earlier with the tripartite squadron, that about fifty knots of forward speed kept the cockpit just sticking out of the great bowl of blowing snow. This was a bit like the bow wave of a ship.

In the tropics what applied to snow, now applied to sand. They were also concerned about the effects on pilots of operating in extremes of temperature. Even in very hot climates pilots have to wear sufficient clothing to enable them to survive ejections at 40,000 feet or so where the temperature is likely to be minus sixty degrees. On the ground, sitting in the cockpit though, the blazing sun can overcook them in that heavy clothing. On sophisticated main bases, they can pump cold air into the cockpit while the pilot is sitting on the ground refuelling or being briefed over the radio. But in the spartan dispersed sites, there were not going to be any aids like that. The answer to that one was delightfully simple —a lady's umbrella, done in a drab, nasty green camouflage paint. The little inexpensive nylon umbrella is in every cockpit and plugs on to the windscreen frame. It must cost all of one pound sterling.

A number of Harriers were lost both during development and in early R.A.F. squadron service, due to power failures. These engine stoppages were matters of desperate concern to a service flying a single engine aircraft. Some were caused in low level flight by birdstrikes in the engine, some by pure mechanical failure like a fan blade breaking. The

third and most worrisome cause was when the complex engine fuel control unit failed to supply the necessary fuel to a
perfectly good engine. This fuel system is a very complicated
affair. It has to control the fuel flow correctly in relation to
speed, r.p.m., altitude and throttle angle, always to provide
the correct thrust. It is not simply a matter of getting more
or less thrust by "winding the wick" up or down on the fuel.
The pilot is given all this automatic control to simplify his
handling task with the airplane. Any malfunction of the various monitoring devices could result in their deciding quite
incorrectly that the engine needed no more fuel when, in
fact, it did. Result—engine failure and loss of aircraft.

Duncan Simpson, then Chief Test Pilot, was a victim of
the fuel system problem on his very first flight in the Harrier
two-seater, shortly after it started flying in 1970. He was at
500 feet in normal straight and level flight over Salisbury
Plain when the engine ran down. He could not restart it and,
at very low altitude, was forced to eject. Simpson was doubly
lucky. Not only did he manage escape from the aircraft, he
also managed to survive his injuries, a broken neck. There
were two schools of thought as to how he was injured. In the
sequence of ejection from the Harrier, the miniature detona-
ting cord in the canopy explodes a hole in the perspex, a split
second before the pilot is blasted out in the rocket seat. One
theory was that somehow a large piece of perspex hit him on
the head. The other theory was that because he bailed out
very low he did not get into a steady parachute descent before he hit the ground. Whatever the cause, the effect was a
broken neck, and Simpson had to undergo a bone graft and
other surgery to put him right. Fortunately, the injuries did
not affect his nervous system. The aircraft, though, was
totally destroyed in the crash, and there were no clues to the
failure in the fuel control unit.

Then, a few months later, test pilot Barry Tonkinson
was flying in another two-seater, again near Boscombe Down,

when the same thing happened. He tried to relight the Pegasus, failed, and without doubt should have pulled the ejection handle. Instead, with great cool and courage, he decided to try to save the aircraft. Boscombe airfield was shut so there were no standby fire crews, but he managed to put the Harrier down on the rough ground beside the runway. The undercarriage broke up on impact, and the Harrier skidded on its belly onto the runway and burst into flames. The lurching, rattling ride after touchdown punched his face about a bit and he was very lucky to undo his harness in his dazed condition and scramble clear. His guts and determination had managed, though, to save the bit of the aircraft that mattered. The fuel system on top of the engine was undamaged. The accident investigation proved that dirt had gotten into the fuel, and blocked a small hole in the system.

The obvious solution was a manually operated fuel system as a standby or backup to the automatic system. The automatic system started with a pump which fed fuel towards the engine through a system of valves, springs and levers, and then on to the burners. The manual system was designed with a pipe which went straight from the engine to the burners, pumping in raw fuel uncontrolled by complex automation. The pilot was given a "tap" in that pipe through which, with careful manipulation, he could carry out all the functions of the automatic system. That was the theory, at any rate. It was asking a bit much, perhaps, but it was better than ejecting.

After a series of ground trials John Farley got airborne, turned off the main fuel control unit, and switched to manual, testing during that sortie to see how fast he could open and close the throttle, at what r.p.m., and so on. He finished by doing an entire sortie on the manual system, including vertical and short takeoffs, accelerating and decelerating transitions. It was hard work making the constant fuel adjustments over the entire speed range by hand, but it could be done.

The main danger was that a pilot might forget momentarily that he was flying on the manual control system, and make an instinctive throttle movement. It might be perfectly permissible on automatic control system, but on manual it could result in an engine flame-out. A so-called fixed throttle landing technique was developed for circumstances where the manual system was in use. The engine was set to 80 percent of its power and then the throttle was left alone.

But how is a pilot to control speed? If he wants to go faster, he diverts the engine thrust backwards by using the nozzle lever. If he wants to slow down, he lowers the nozzles the required amount. It is not advised to try a vertical landing on manual, but if there is no choice, then he hovers it as normal and uses very slow, very gentle throttle movements.

The manual system has saved a lot of airplanes. Just after it was fitted to the famous Harrier two-seat demonstrator GVTOL, Farley was in the back seat with a Swiss evaluation pilot in the front, doing "circuit bashing" or practice landings and takeoffs at Dunsfold. The Swiss pilots were used to jets with much less performance than the Harrier, and they were very reluctant to climb steeply enough and throttle back sufficiently to cut down noise on takeoff over Dunsfold village. They were inhibited from raising the nose and reducing power for fear of losing speed and stalling. On that particular day, the Swiss pilot, who was preparing for his first solo in a jump jet, did in fact appear to throttle back at around 200 feet. The Harrier had just started flying on its wings, and Farley immediately thought that the man in the front seat had throttled back far too much. Knowing that instructors destroy a pupil's confidence if they take control immediately, the vastly experienced Farley, who spends much of his test flying deliberately letting aircraft misbehave, waited and waited. The engine r.p.m. wound down and down, right through 55 per cent. He was just about to tell the Swiss on the intercom that he should open the throttle, when the

The famous Harrier two-seat demonstrator G-VTOL, owned by British Aerospace shown in a steep John Farley climb-out from the VTOL pad in a clump of trees at Dunsfold Airfield.

Swiss pilot barked, "I have lost ze throttle!" Farley looked down at his dual control and saw that the other pilot was banging it back and forward without any effect. The fuel system had failed. It was a desperate situation. The Harrier had sunk during these few seconds to just above the trees, beyond the end of the runway. Farley switched to manual from the back cockpit, and the Pegasus roared into life and rose from the trees, bearing two very relieved pilots. It had been a last ditch gamble before using the rocket ejection seats to blast themselves 400 feet above a doomed aircraft. The changeover from normal to manual fuel system had never been done before with the throttle most of the way forward and the engine still winding down, but it had worked. Life for a test pilot has its frustrations the same as any other. But they could never claim it was boring.

In later years the Harrier program was to be held up by a former Permanent Secretary to the Ministry of Aviation as an example of an aircraft program which did not follow the cliche that it overran on cost, was late on delivery, and did not do what the customers had specified. The Harrier was delivered within cost, to specification and on time. The makers said the first Harrier would be flying by August 1966, and it was a matter of professional pride rather than contractual obligation that they determined to meet their self-imposed deadline. Luckily, August had thirty-one days, for they just made it in time.

It was around seven o'clock and the sun was low in the sky that evening of August 31, 1966. In the experimental hangar at Dunsfold, the first Harrier XV 276 sat, unpainted, with swarms of people still working all around her, signing forms, putting on panels. Watching all this activity with a particularly sharp eye was an official Ministry aircraft inspector. It was his job to make sure that the aircraft was indeed airworthy before the first flight could take place, and he was very concerned about the fact that the cockpit was incomplete. There were a couple of panel covers missing opposite where the pilot puts his feet, before he places them on the rudder bar. It was the inspector's head on the block if anything went wrong as a result of incompleted work, and he was digging his heels in: "You can't possibly fly it in that state. You could catch your boots in the exposed structure." The panels had not even been manufactured at that stage, which placed Bill Bedford and Chief Designer John Fozard in a delicate position. It took a lot of charm and persuasion to convince the nervous inspector that Bedford would not lift his feet from the rudder bar, and the man signed the release

form. It was now almost dark, just after eight o'clock, but
there was still a glow from the setting sun, and the sky was
clear. Bedford switched on the navigation lights, taxied out
and took off vertically. He simply sat there in the hover for
five minutes, slightly dazzled by the unshielded array of
colored cockpit lights. Then he put the aircraft down again.
The Harrier had flown for the first time.

Fozard's elation was a little tempered when a senior
man in the Ministry of Aviation said crushingly, "All right,
you say you flew it within the time you promised. But you
didn't really fly it, did you? You only hovered!" To have to
explain at that stage of the game that hovering was what
VTOL was all about, was really a bit much, Fozard and his
colleagues thought.

The aircraft met the operational requirement set out for
it by the Royal Air Force. Extraordinary though it may
seem, the attitude of the Air Staff, the R.A.F.'s decision
makers, was, to say the least, lukewarm. As we know, they
wanted more Phantoms instead of the Harrier. It was foisted
upon them, it was subsonic, and they did not think it was
going to carry enough weapons. The vulnerability of runways
and the advantages of an aircraft they could disperse were
not potent enough factors to allay their disappointment at
Mr. Healey's decision. In all fairness, they were just going
through an unhappy experience with their air defense supersonic interceptor, the Lightning. The Lightning was essentially an experimental aircraft which had been taken into service with a minimum of further development. Its shortage of
endurance was an acute embarrassment. Were they not likely
to face problems with *this* revolutionary new aircraft which
was being added to their inventory? Experience has shown
that they were wrong. But one of the principal reasons for
the change in attitude towards V/STOL in the senior levels
of the Royal Air Force now, is that the young officers who
helped pioneer the concept back in the earliest days are now

themselves just a step or two away from the highest positions in the Service. However, the fact remains that, apart from a significant few, the Air Force of the country which gave birth to the world's first production V/STOL fighter have little cause to congratulate themselves on their part in helping this unique airplane to survive and flourish.

The biggest injection of life and bounding enthusiasm which the Harrier ever received was when three officers of the U.S. Marine Corps walked into the Hawker Siddeley chalet at the 1968 Farnborough Air Show and told astonished executives: "We want to fly your airplane." It was the start of the most exciting period in the Harrier's development.

Chapter 8

The U.S. Marines Enter the Story

The Marines bought the Harrier "off the shelf" from Britain. With a mixture of political skill, hard work and sheer enthusiasm, they persuaded the men on Capitol Hill that they should be allowed to buy this revolutionary foreign airplane. It was the first time since the First World War that any American armed service had bought an aircraft that was not manufactured in the United States. The unpalatable fact was that the vast American aerospace industry had been quite unable to come up with anything which began to match the Harrier. The Marines drew on their score of affection and respect and said, "This is the airplane we need. This is the airplane we must have." They have a reputation for getting what they want from defense budgets because they never normally ask for too much. However, this was no ordinary request. There was the obvious political complication of buying a military aircraft outside their own country. They also had to persuade the Navy, who procure aircraft for the Marines through their Naval Air Systems Command. For a service which had always had to accept the aircraft which the Navy decided they should fly, what the Marines were attempting was a truly radical departure.

The Marine Corps had been interested in V/STOL since the mid-40's when helicopters first demonstrated to them the basing flexibility which did not require large landing fields or prepared landing sites. In the Pacific campaign during World War II, Marine air and Marine ground troops were separated for long periods because of lack of airfields on the islands where amphibious assaults were launched. It was an unacceptable situation to the Corps whose air and ground forces are quite unique in that, if they are to be effective, they are quite inseparable. Marines on the ground lack the organic firepower which ordinary infantry units have, and much of their firepower is dependent on their own pilots, under the control of their own commander, flying close support missions. In action, they fiercely resist any attempt to use Marine air power for any other function than supporting the "grunts" on the ground.

As the years went by, the situation worsened. Ship to shore naval gunfire support decreased as missiles were introduced. Aircraft from other services, particularly the Navy, were less and less available as jets were introduced and bomb loads went down. At the same time, the worldwide commitments of the Marine Corps were increasing. They were becoming more expeditionary, more scattered, yet ever more dependent upon their airpower to support any amphibious operation. As a consequence, they launched into a very intensive effort to make their aviation units fully expeditionary. The basis of this was the expeditionary airfield, made from aluminum matting which could be transported ashore and assembled in the absence of suitable fixed airfields. They continued to some extent with the World War II system of rocket bottles for jet assisted short takeoff, though this aid could be dangerous and was a very expensive one-shot affair each time. They developed arresting gear for short landings, to help minimize the runway length of the expeditionary airfield. It was a successful redesign of the Navy gear, and is still in use today.

A requirement was laid down that all Marine tactical aircraft had to be able to take off with a useful combat load in 4,000 feet. So, the Marines' answer had come down to building these 4,000 foot runways wherever they went and recovering their aircraft using arrester gear. A requirement had been written by the long term planners back in 1958 for a fixed wing high performance V/STOL aircraft, and it seemed that if someone could come up with a viable machine then they could do away with expeditionary runways altogether.

The Marine Corps, of course, had not participated in the tripartite V/STOL evaluation squadron. They decided that the aircraft's potential at that time was far too limited in terms of payload. It seemed to them that the Kestrel was going to need a lot of research and development money, and they are not in the research and development business. Any aircraft they buy or that are procured for them by the Navy have got to be capable of purchase straight "off the shelf" without further development costs. They kept a close watch on the Kestrel reports, though, for it was still the most promising looking V/STOL aircraft around. It was simple in principle, and it looked like an attack aircraft, not a research vehicle. Many of the programs being investigated by U.S. manufacturers seemed far too complex. They had an assortment of fuselages and wings and all sorts of contraptions to give V/STOL performance, to the point where they had no military significance at all.

Then the British government announced in 1965, their intention to develop the Kestrel into the Harrier, and the Marines started to take a much closer interest. What spurred them into positive action was a promotional film on the Harrier made by Hawker Siddeley in 1968. The senior officers who watched it could hardly believe that an aircraft could perform in that way. The aircraft hovered, it did transitions and high speed runs, and the marvellous simplicity of the nozzle system was explained. For those who were basing their attitudes on the Kestrel performance data, the statistics were a revelation. The Pegasus engine had been increased by 4,000 pounds in thrust to 19,000 pounds. The difference between that and the weight of the aircraft meant around 6,000 pounds to trade off between fuel and ordnance.

The Vietnam war was at its height then, in 1968, and the average bomb load being carried by the Marines' light attack aircraft, the A4 Skyhawk, was around 3,000 pounds. Splitting the Harrier payload roughly fifty–fifty between fuel and ordnance would give around the same bomb load as the Skyhawk, a radius of action of thirty-five–fifty miles and up to five minutes over the target. That assumed a vertical takeoff by the Harrier, which in terms of quick response was the obvious way of operating it. But, it could also take off conventionally, of course, and they then overlaid the Harrier and Skyhawk in this mode. From its minimum takeoff distance of around 3,000 feet the Skyhawk would carry the same load as the Harrier from its very short conventional takeoff of 500 feet. There was not going to be any problem in finding 500 feet of straight country road anywhere in the world.

The late Major General Keith B. McCutcheon was at that time running the Marine Corps aviation. He was Deputy Chief of Staff (Air) at Marine Corps H. Q. in Washington. When the lights went up after the movie, he turned to the other aviators in the room and said: "That looks like the thing we've been looking for." Someone went and dusted down the 1958 V/STOL operational requirement file.

General McCutcheon authorized Colonel Tom Miller and Colonel Bud Baker to fly to England and look at the aircraft performing at the international Farnborough Air Show near London. History has shown that it was an important decision,

Lt. Gen. Tom Miller, Jr., United States Marine Corps, who "sold" the Harrier concept to the Corps after his evaluation of the aircraft in England in 1968.

but the visit nearly did not take place because the Marines' shoestring budget did not seem capable of bearing the two officers' travel costs! They arrived on September 1, planning to stay for a week. They were there for seventeen days, and when they returned to America they were utterly convinced it was the aircraft for the Marines.

The U.S. Navy is responsible for procurement, research and development of Marine Corps aircraft, and for obvious reasons they have always been anxious to get as much "commonality" between the two services as possible. The Marines anticipated trouble from their "big brother," if and when they finally decided to ask the Navy to procure this new airplane for them. After all, the Navy at that time had no requirement for V/STOL, and the inclusion of the Harrier into the Navy/Marines inventory could not be further from the concept of commonality. Thus, there was considerable secrecy in the run up to the Farnborough Air Show. It was not underhanded, but the Marines wanted to have "all their ducks lined up" before they asked for a decision. So, they did not even tell Vice Admiral Tom Connolly, the Deputy Chief of Naval Operations for Air Warfare. Ironically, Connolly was to turn out to be a consistent champion of the Marines' request for the aircraft. They did not want Hawker Siddeley, the manufacturers, to know how intense their interest was. British Embassy officials in Washington asked technical questions on the Harrier and fed back the answers off the record to people like Colonel Miller and General McCutcheon. Although Hawker Siddeley knew the Marines would be at Farnborough, the intensity of their interest came as a shock. The two colonels and a Marine Corps one star general (Johnson) walked into the aircraft company's chalet and said, "We want to fly the Harrier." Tom Miller asked for a set of pilot's notes, and on the last day of the show, the Ministry of Defense gave permission for the Marines to have ten flights each. They spent many hours discussing the aircraft with people like Fozard, Hooper, Merewether and Bedford. At the start of the second week, they were at Dunsfold to start flying.

England was being drenched with rain and there was widespread flooding. Over Dunsfold for the first two days there was constant drizzle and very low cloud ceilings, so they spent their time going over and over the flying characteristics with test pilot John Farley. By Wednesday, the weather had not improved much, but they were impatient to get on with it, so they started some high-speed taxiing. The 6,000 feet of runway seemed a very short distance as they accelerated up to 120 knots then put the nozzles into the braking stop to slow down and stop. There was a lot to do in the cockpit, but these runs built up their confidence in controlling the Harrier. Seeing the end of the runway racing towards them, there was sometimes a tendency to apply too much throttle in the braking stop. It was a little difficult then to know whether or not they were airborne as they floated like a ping-pong ball in the airstream. On one of his first runs Colonel Baker pulled the nose up to try to decelerate and touched the tail on the ground. By Thursday morning it was still overcast, but they decided to carry out their first hovers. Tom Miller was first and "poured the coal on" as briefed. The Harrier was reluctant to leave the ground, then lifted off slowly to about fifteen feet. It then started going up like a cork out of a champagne bottle. The cloud layer at 300 feet seemed to be racing down to meet him, and Miller didn't think it was a very good idea to fly on instruments only, on his first hover! As he put it, "I found myself pulling off throttle, kinda rapidly but slowly, if you understand." The Harrier stopped ascending just as the canopy brushed the cloud ceiling. Miller found the vertical takeoff incredibly smooth with none of the vibration he had experienced in helicopters. And, of course, the noise of the engine did not affect him in the cocoon of the cockpit. He felt so much at home that John Farley called him from the ground, on radio, and suggested he might like to give Bud Baker a turn. He climbed from the cockpit feeling thoroughly intoxicated by it. He'd never experienced anything quite like it.

However, as trained test pilots, both Miller and Baker had to curb their exuberance. They still had not tested the conventional aspects of the aircraft which had to measure up if they were ever to contemplate buying it. For the rest of the time, they ran the gamut, including practice attacks, some of them using the nozzles to slow the aircraft down. They also asked Hawker to provide them with a flight envelope within which they could experiment with putting the nozzles down in conventional flight, to try to improve their maneuverability in air combat. From the reaction the American pilots got, they assumed they were the first ever to ask permission to use the airplane in this way. The manufacturers computed speed and engine ranges, and at around 25,000 feet and 300 knots, Miller and Baker made the first hesitant steps towards thrust vectoring in flight—a facility which the Marine Corps pilots have since developed into a potent dog-fighting weapon.

At the end of their trip, they were both completely convinced that the Harrier was the airplane for the Marine Corps. Skeptics said prior to their trip, that the V/STOL capability of the Harrier would inevitably mean that it could not carry much weight of fuel or armaments, never mind what the manufacturers were claiming. Their test flying proved this simply was not true. It was at least equivalent, in those respects to the Skyhawk, and that was an airplane which was universally liked by Marine pilots.

On their journey home from England, Miller and Baker decided on a strategy for the briefings they would have to give on their return. They decided to adopt a low key, conservative posture to dispel any illusions that exuberance over a revolutionary aircraft had overcome their common sense approach to a piece of potential military equipment.

Colonel Miller was slated to give a briefing to General Chapman, Commandant of the Marine Corps, at 2:00 P.M. on September 24. That morning he got a telephone call from a friend in the powerful President's Scientific Advisory Group who heard about his trip to England. The Group consists mainly of highly educated aerodynamicists, physicists, mathematicians from industry whose job is to give the president a viewpoint from outside the immediate military sphere. They weren't pilots but they were very familiar with the technical aspects and design criteria of military aircraft. The Group sat around with their feet on the table eating lunch from their brown bags as Miller briefed them on the Harrier.

The principal thrust of their questioning was: Does the Harrier have enough power to get off the ground vertically? Would it have enough time on station to do an effective military job? Tom Miller quoted the figures compared with the Skyhawk, but pointed out that in fact the VTO fifty mile radius he mentioned was probably a far greater distance than the aircraft would ever be asked to fly because its flexibility would allow it to be close to the battle. It looked as if they could increase the bomb load or the fuel and give the airplane that much more freedom of action. The Group had been impressed in the past by the way the Marines had sponsored the use of the military helicopter. There was no doubt from their reaction that this powerful caucus was very excited by Tom Miller's one-and-a-half-hour briefing. Before the political battle even started, he had won some formidable allies.

General Chapman listened carefully to his briefing by Colonel Miller and simply said: "Tom, this sounds like the aircraft we've really been looking for. Don't you think we ought to get some?" The decision was made. It really had been an awesome responsibility that had been placed on the shoulders of one full colonel, that of assessing and then recommending within such a short time whether or not to purchase a wholly revolutionary new aircraft. Time, though, was of the essence, for when General Chapman took Tom Miller's advice, the defense budget negotiations for the following year, 1969, had almost been completed. The pressure was on to get the budget to the printer in time for Congress in January. The scramble to get the request for Harriers into the budget began. It was to be a revolution in bureaucratic paperwork for Washington, D.C.

From the time of his return from England, Tom Miller entered into one of the busiest periods of his life. He now began to draw upon the political skills that he had built up over years of experience with congressional hearings and the close interrelation between the military and industry. Remember that what the Marines were proposing was inevitably going to take millions of dollars worth of business away from the American aircraft industry, much of which had been trying to produce a V/STOL production aircraft itself. Miller steeled himself and set off on the rounds of the aircraft factories, briefing presidents, vice presidents and leading engineers. It would not have been surprising, had they decided to ask their state politicians to block this deal on their behalf. The essence of Miller's argument was that something like half a billion dollars had been spent in the United States which had produced nothing apart from a number of very sophisticated, unusable machines. For the aircraft companies to block the deal would be to stand in the way of V/STOL development, he argued. That he succeeded is both a tribute to his own personal qualities and to the magnanimous acceptance by the American industry that they could not come up with a viable production V/STOL aircraft within a sensible time scale.

His principal concerns were the Ryan Aircraft Corporation and McDonnell Douglas. Ryan was probably further along the road to V/STOL than anyone else in America at that time with their XV5 which had lift fans in the wing, and had already done a fair amount of test flying. A letter from the vice president of Ryan was later produced during a congressional hearing. "After going over the British Harrier proposal, I reverse my opinion and think a buy of them would be the best way to get V/STOL rolling in America. We or another manufacturer could build a better airplane, but development costs would be between 300 and 400 million dollars. Most of that would be to design a good fighter system and not because of the vertical characteristics. If you can get these for fifty or sixty million dollars, we should go ahead to prove or disprove V/STOL instead of just talking about it." Inevitably, the letter had tried to save some face for the Ryan product, but it was also a very candid admission of the lead that Britain had in the field.

McDonnell Douglas was a potential problem for another reason. The first U.S.M.C. buy was going to be only twelve aircraft, costing fifty-six million dollars. It was not going to help them politically to ask for additional dollars on top of their budget, so there had to be some pruning. They decided to scrub seventeen brand new McDonnell Douglas Phantoms, as evidence of the internal sacrifice they were prepared to make, to provide for this first buy of Harriers. It also meant that McDonnell was about to lose fifty-six million dollars.

Tom Miller clearly had a lot of persuasive talking to do. He was a Phantom pilot himself and had in fact worked closely with McDonnell as a research and development project officer on the Phantom. He knew the top management well but was under no illusion that it would be an easy task. He told them that he recognized the difficulty of their position, but that in the long run this Marine Corps involvement in V/STOL would benefit aviation generally in America. And, although he had no authority to say it (and McDonnell knew it, too) he told them that, in his opinion, the aircraft's future development would bring a great deal of work back to St. Louis. This is exactly what did happen, with the license agreement between the two companies, and later the development of the advanced version of the aircraft. At that time, it was an act of faith on the part of McDonnell Douglas. Plus, of course, the almost certain knowledge that the government would place part of the work with American companies. At the end of Miller's lobbying campaign, the Marines had the solid backing of the American aircraft industry for their plans. It was a major achievement. The next important goal was Congress and the Senate.

In those days, the budget left the Department of the Navy in July, the Department of Defense in September and the Office of Management and Budget around October. Once the budget "went to bed" it was generally unchangeable, but the Marine Corps Headquarters staff literally worked day and night in their determination not to have to wait until the next fiscal year for approval. The big stumbling block was the systems analysis branch of the Department of Defense. They felt it was rushing things too much, that the proposals needed much more scrutiny, and they dug their heels in to the extent that the budget was printed for Congress without the application for Harriers.

The Marines refused to be beaten, and it was at this stage, that the enormous esteem in which General McCutcheon was held by the establishment began to pay dividends. The feeling was that if General McCutcheon genuinely believed that the Marines needed this airplane that much, then whatever the systems analysis people were saying, the Marines ought to be allowed to procure it. The head of the President's Scientific Advisory Group put his weight behind it, the objections were overruled, and a special amendment was printed and tacked onto the budget. It had meant that every level in government which was involved in the budgeting process had had to stop, backtrack, and move money around to accommodate the Marines. It was unprecedented, but somehow they managed it. Despite the odds, there had never really been much doubt in the minds of the Marines that they would.

The hearings before Congress commenced in March 1969. In the run-up to the hearings, the Marines had been briefing the politicians just as busily as the industrialists. Staff members of the various committees—House Armed Services, House Appropriations, Senate Armed Services and Senate Appropriations—were all given thorough and sometimes lengthy briefings on the proposed Harrier program. Mr. Russ Blandford, Chief Counsel of the House Armed Services Committee was particularly interested as a Marine reserve officer, and he advised Mr. Mendel Rivers, head of the committee. Promisingly, there was no opposition amongst the staff advisors.

The Marines' campaign got an unexpected shot in the arm when two R.A.F. Harriers remained in the United States after the Daily Mail Transatlantic Air Race. Using in-flight refuelling, the Harriers, which had only been in R.A.F. squadron service for a few weeks, achieved pad-to-pad times of five hours fifty-seven minutes westbound and five hours thirty-one minutes eastbound from London G.P.O. tower to the Empire State Building in New York. The westbound flight was the fastest overall for the Race, and it was a proud achievement for the 3,030 nautical mile distance. No one

John Fozard, former Harrier Chief Designer (center), pictured beside the R.A.F. Harrier which was demonstrated at St. Louis in 1970 after hot weather trials at Yuma, Arizona. Also pictured is Mr. James S. McDonnell, founder of the McDonnell Douglas Corporation.

celebrating the triumph realized just how close the aircraft had come to disaster.

Hawker Siddeley cleared the Harrier for various aspects of long duration flight, like oxygen reserves, oil consumption and, critically, flight refuelling. Hawker's test pilots had specifically flown sorties of up to seven hours to test these features, and everyone was confident that the Harrier was up to the task. Any failure in flight refuelling during the Transatlantic dash would have sent the aircraft into the sea and, quite apart from the likelihood of losing the pilots, the damage to the aircraft's and the service's prestige would have been enormous. So, it did make the odd hair stand up on the back of the neck when, shortly after the race, further flight refuelling tests, at Boscombe Down, resulted in a pipe bursting in the Harrier under pressure from the tanker aircraft. It didn't really bear thinking about. But every new aircraft needs its share of luck, and all Harriers were swiftly modified to prevent a recurrence.

With both Harriers conveniently in America, it was decided to put on a demonstration for Senators and Congressmen who were specially flown to Andrews Air Force Base. The two Harriers were "owned" by Group Captain, now Air Vice Marshal, Peter Williamson who was later to become commander of the first Harrier squadron at R.A.F. station Wittering. There was a small ground crew who never worked on the airplane before, and the two pilots were John Farley and Squadron Leader Tom Leckey Thomson, one of the Air Race pilots. It was a marvelous opportunity at this politically sensitive time, to show some of the most powerful people in America just what the British aircraft could do.

John Farley recalls that if the American authorities had had any inkling of just how far out on a limb the Harriers were operating, then they would probably have withdrawn their permission for the demonstration that was about to take place. They may have been operating from the middle of

Andrews Air Force Base, but with an inexperienced ground crew and no V/STOL backup facilities if anything should go wrong, Farley felt they might as well have been operating from the moon. However, he and others felt strongly that the demonstration was the proper thing to do. The Harrier was now a production aircraft, and though it had not had the chance to prove itself in service, Hawker Siddeley would not have gone into service with it if they were not confident that they had ironed out the kinks.

Part of the demonstration was to be a flight on to a flat top ship with an engine shutdown then a restart and vertical takeoff. Farley felt that if they could not do these relatively straightforward things, then they really should not be trying to sell it. These feelings were not universally shared in the company, however. Understandably, some people back in England, who had been through all the traumas of the aircraft's development, were a little "twitchy" about the appalling prospect, however slight, of some humiliating failure in such an important showcase. As the little jet began its performance, the grins of disbelief from the distinguished audience dispelled anyone's doubts.

The politicians and senior officers from all the armed services had been ferried out to an aircraft carrier off Norfolk, Virginia. Moored nearby was the U.S.S. *La Salle*, a landing platform dock ship, with a small helicopter platform aft. Farley took off from Andrews Base, landed vertically on the *La Salle*, and shut down the engine. Rocket pods and fuel tanks were loaded on to the underwing pylons. He took a deep breath and, very conscious of the watching crowd, he pressed the self-starter. The Pegasus came to life and the Harrier lifted smoothly upwards, the bulk of its warload dramatically deepen its head-on view as it accelerated into wingborne flight.

The demonstration had a profound psychological effect on many of the onlookers. Quite apart from the unique spec-

tacle of this jet landing and taking off vertically, they had
never seen a front line combat airplane that did not need
flight deck equipment to start the engine. It was one of
several Harrier features, including the nosewheel steering and
the head-up display, of which American pilots had written,
"Should be incorporated in all future design of all airplanes,
not just jump jets." It seemed to some of the Hawker
Siddeley people that by the simple act of letting people see
it fly, the Harrier would virtually sell itself. This optimism
was understandable, but not all the politicians were so easily
swayed in favor of the Marines' Harrier purchase.

Senator Symington, one of the two senators from
Missouri, home of McDonnell Douglas, told Colonel Miller
frankly, "You know, Tom, I don't know how you can honestly expect me to support this program when you think of
what it's going to do to my people at McDonnell's." Tom
Miller had made his trip to the factory in St. Louis by this
time, and he suggested that the senator talk with the McDonnell people again. Significantly, he did not oppose the final
budget vote, though his questions were frequently searching
during the hearings.

A look at the record of the Congressional and Senate
budget hearings gives a fascinating glimpse of the determination of the politicans to satisfy themselves that there was no
viable American alternative. It also gives an insight into both
the political skills of the Marine Corps leaders and their iron
determination to see their program through.

Monday, May 12, 1969, House Appropriations Committee:

> MR. SIKES: In what respects do the aircraft in this general
> area which have been developed in the United States fail
> to meet the requirements that you expect to acquire in
> the Harrier? In other words, I find it hard to understand
> when we have been putting money into this concept
> for twenty-odd years to my own knowledge, that we

come up with nothing that is usable, and we have to go overseas to buy the aircraft. Whose fault is that?

GENERAL McCUTCHEON: I don't think it is anybody's fault, Mr. Sikes. I think in this country the particular techniques that were used and investigated to get the V/STOL did not pan out as well as the vectored thrust principle that is used in the Harrier's engine. We had twelve or fifteen different developments in this country, including tilt wings, tilt engines, fan jets, and so forth. Of these, I guess the fan jet shows about as much promise as any.

MR. SIKES: Did we try to develop in too broad an area? Did we scatter our shot too much? In what way did we fail to accomplish what was desired? I still have not had an answer as to why all this development effort in the United States was unproductive and we had to go overseas to buy an aircraft.

GENERAL McCUTCHEON: This is a new area. When we started into it nobody knew exactly what the final outcome would produce, so they more or less had to shoot across a broad spectrum and try all those approaches that appeared technically feasible. The fact that this one surpassed all the others, accounts for the successful accomplishment of the Harrier.

MR. SIKES: What is the nearest aircraft with capabilities such as the Harrier which has been developed in the United States?

GENERAL McCUTCHEON: If you concentrate on the VTOL there is none, but the closest would be the Ryan fan jet development.

MR. SIKES: Why could it not have been given the incentive necessary to place it in the same favorable light the Harrier now enjoys, if that type is what we want?

GENERAL McCUTCHEON: It probably could have if it had received more emphasis in the past. Still, with proper emphasis, it could still be an airplane in the future. The point is that right now they do not have the aircraft flying.

MR. SIKES: Over what period of time could a satisfactory aircraft be developed by an American firm?

GENERAL McCUTCHEON: It is estimated that it would take at least five years and probably seven.

Later in the hearing, Vice Admiral Tom Connolly, Deputy Chief of Operations for Air Warfare, and a member of the procurement executive for the Harrier, was equally adamant that there was no alternative to the Harrier.

MR. LIPSCOMB: I have two observations. Maybe you can comment on them, if you desire. It appears to me that on transactions of this sort, the United States always gets the short end of the deal. Second, it is almost inconceivable, in my mind, that it is necessary for the United States with its great technological ability in manufacturing and development to find it necessary to go to Great Britain to get a plane such as the Harrier. I just cannot understand this, and I cannot in good conscience support this particular purchase from this side of the table.

ADMIRAL CONNOLLY: I do not want always to be saying things that are contrary to your impressions. I certainly cannot comment on the first part of your statement. You know far better than I about that. Yet it is not without good precedent that where the British have concentrated and worked hard, they have come up with things that we have not. After all Pratt and Whitney would not be developing the turbojet and turbofan today if they had not had a license from Rolls Royce in the beginning and learned to build it. General Motors, as big as it is and as great as it is, and with its Allison Division going back so many years, in order to get back into the jet engine business had to become a licensee for the TF41 and other Rolls Royce engines.

I know that you're aware that the British in their own way came up with the steam catapult, the angled deck and the mirror landing system. While we were so busy moving our carriers around the ocean, into the Mediterranean and out West, they, without funds and striving and struggling, did come up with these concepts as they have with some other things. They have concentrated on this type of airplane.

I approached this whole thing as a complete agnostic. When General McCutcheon came over and said they (the Marines) wanted this, I thought he had lost his mind. As we got into it and conducted the Navy Preliminary Evaluation one of the test pilots who had fighter experience in Vietnam came back and said: 'I will take on any fighter out there today with the Harrier and I know I'll beat him.' In fact, one gentleman who may be in the audience said he would give anybody tail position, and he would take the Harrier and get round on him.

It does hurt a little to realize that these people have come up with something that we couldn't, but we would spend millions of dollars and much time going back to Ryan or anybody else to do it now. It seems to me it would be a great waste. We have put so much into Britain. We have helped them for a long time as you well know. This (the Harrier) is something that they have, and it does seem to me that that island over there would be a liability to us if they didn't stand on their own two feet. This (aircraft) and the engine are the only things I know of that they have come up with in a long time.

Any red-blooded Briton might have taken issue with the last remark, but Admiral Connolly was, in fact, a great friend of the Harrier program.

The Marines wanted 114 aircraft and that was the number they eventually got, but the first year's buy was only twelve. The unique situation transpired that while they were debating the Marines' request up on the Hill, a Naval preliminary evaluation team was actually in Britain flying the aircraft. This meant that the political decision was not dependent upon the Navy evaluation. The politicians were obliged to make up their minds while this was going on. It was an unheard of situation, and some people in Congress were unhappy about it. They wanted the twelve aircraft bought and evaluated in the normal way and if the Harrier was then found suitable they could come back and ask for more.

The problem for the Marines was that any order they placed then, in 1969, would not be delivered until 1971 and a proper evaluation would not be completed until around the spring of 1972. As things stood at that time Hawker Siddeley anticipated that their production of the Harrier Mark I for the R.A.F. would be finished then. If the Marines then decided they wanted more, Hawker Siddeley might not have been able to reopen their production line. The Secretary of the Navy stepped in and decided that since the R.A.F. had accepted it for their use, he would waive some normal requirements and rely mainly on evaluation data already gathered from the Government Test Establishment at Boscombe Down in England. This, combined with the information being transmitted from the Navy evaluation team in England, gave the Marines sufficiently convincing technical arguments to put to the committees.

In their budget request for the financial year 1970, the Marines put in a five-year defense plan for 114 Harriers in all to equip three tactical squadrons and one training squadron. It put the minds of Congress at rest because it meant that each year the Marines would have to produce the evidence that the aircraft was performing to expectations before more dollars were allocated for the next buy. The Marines' stated intention was that the advanced Harrier, the AV-8B, would eventually total 336, replacing the Skyhawk, and the present Harrier (AV-8A) squadrons. It will mean that by the late 1980s all five Skyhawk squadrons will have been replaced by AV-8B's, and then the existing three AV-8A squadrons will themselves be phased out and replaced with their more advanced brother. The all-weather A6 attack squadrons will remain, but by that time the Marines hope to have become an all V/STOL light attack force.

Air Commodore Eric Burchmore, an R.A.F. engineering officer was the director of the Harrier program for the U.K. government when the Navy evaluation team came to England. They were accompanied by a negotiating team led by Marine Corps Colonel Ed Harper, the very experienced A4 program manager. At a private function, General McCutcheon virtually pleaded with Burchmore to keep the Marine Corps program on time and running smoothly right from the outset. Burchmore was under great pressure to get the R.A.F. aircraft perfected according to the stringent service specification and into service on time. It was felt, however, that as the deal was going to be on a government to government basis it would be best to have the same man managing both programs. Burchmore and his team had not even completed the testing against the specification on the British aircraft at that stage, yet they were being asked by Ed Harper and the Marines and U.S. Navy delegation to provide a separate, guaranteed specification for the American airplane. Of course, it was to be an "off-the-shelf" buy without further development, but the American form of specification tends to be much more complex and lengthy than the British. The Marines knew that without this detailed specification they could not "sell" that first year buy anywhere in Washington.

Burchmore knew that all the necessary data on the aircraft had not been gathered, but hand on heart he drew up a full specification for the budgetary hearings, as if all the information were available. It was living just a little dangerously, but he had no choice under the circumstances. There was never any doubt in his mind that the Harrier would meet the specification he promised. Well, not much doubt anyway! Burchmore flew to Washington where he met Colonel Cliff Lindell of the Marine Corps, who was working in Naval Air Systems Command, the Marines' procurement agency. It was an open secret about the preparation of the specification, and the appropriate naval captain would only sign it after Cliff Lindell had signed a certificate of indemnity protecting the captain if anything should go wrong.

Spare parts are vital to the success of any aircraft program, and when it is a foreign airplane, the need for continuity of supply makes it a highly charged political issue. There was a genuine and understandable fear that a war or even sustained industrial trouble in Britain could ground the Marines' aircraft through lack of spares. The attitude was best summed up by Mr. Mendel Rivers, chairman of the House Armed Services Committee: "Let's not get caught in that problem. He who controls the spare parts, controls the war." The original plan had been that Britain would support them for the first eighteen months with the various manufacturers involved sending spares to a bonded warehouse in America. The intention was that gradually the Americans would take over, but the Navy decided that the Marines would support themselves with spares from the outset. At the meeting when this was announced, Burchmore was furious and made a formal protest. In his opinion, the decision could seriously affect the Harrier's chances of succeeding in America. The Americans made their own assessment of needs based on the Skyhawk provisioning program, and Burchmore protested, in vain, that they were underestimating on things like the number of wings they would need.

They also decided to gear themselves to do repairs on components at the Marine air base at Cherry Point in North Carolina. This was not an unqualified success either, and the British firms were continually having to bail them out. The aircraft was dangerously poised many times to be badly let down because of the spares problem, and the budget delays caused by the Vietnam war did not help either. The British companies making the spares could not stand the financial strain of these hold-ups in payment. On one occasion, Burchmore was instructed to fly to Washington to stave off a crisis. On arrival at Dulles airport, he was driven in a staff car at high speed along the hard shoulder of the freeway. Secretary of the Navy John Warner and the Deputy Secretary, Frank Sanders, were waiting in their office. The R. A. F. man told them politely but firmly that he had instructions—no money, no more spares. The money swiftly appeared. That particular cliff-hanger occurred in 1972, and it highlighted the spares difficulties at a time when the airplane was about to face one of its most difficult political hurdles.

The incremental system of procurement meant that there was a real threat of problems for the Harrier program, and its reputation was laid on the line during the third year buy. The chairman of the powerful House Appropriations Committee, Congressman Mahon from Texas, wrote to the Secretary of Defense and made a perfectly valid point for a responsible guardian of the public purse. Why, he wanted to know, was it necessary to buy the Harrier for the Marines, the Cheyenne helicopter for the Army, and the AX, later to be called the A10, for the Air Force? They were all designed after all for the close support role, so why could they not be pared down to two or maybe even one for use by all three services? The Department of Defense, after an exhaustive paper study concluded that all three were, in fact, necessary.

The Deputy Secretary of Defense, Mr. David Packard, thought that there were several weaknesses in each of the three systems. Before he would authorize procurement, he wanted proof that they could carry out the mission they promised. The Marines had claimed that the short distances the Harrier would have to fly would result in a very efficient, very high sortie rate airplane. During the Vietnam war, the Air Force achieved an average of one sortie per plane, per day while the Marines did a little better in Southeast Asia, averaging between 1.2–1.5 per plane, per day. During the Six Day war, the Israelis achieved sortie rates of six and seven a day, though, of course, that was a surge, not sustained long-term effort. The Marines' claim for the Harrier had been that they could manage four sorties a day at a sustained rate, and six during a surge. Secretary Packard insisted that they validate this in a test run under the auspices of the Weapons System Evaluation Group (WESAG). The sortie validation tests were scheduled for several weeks during March of 1972 at Camp Lejeune in North Carolina.

Privately, the Marine aviators were not quite so confident that they would meet their predicted sortie rate. They only had nine aircraft at that stage, and they had to be really well supported in parts and maintenance, if they were not to fall flat on their faces. They ran a model of the proposed tests through a computer and calculated the amount of spares they would need. As the tests got under way, Marines were in around-the-clock telephone contact with England ordering vital spares and meeting them off aircraft to be rushed to Camp Lejeune.

The tests were really a bit like a lie-detector test. Pass it, and it does not help that much, but fail it, and there is trouble. In the event, the Marines surprised everyone, including themselves. Operating out of two dispersed sites they achieved a sustained rate of six sorties a day and a surge of ten. In fact, they cut off the flying to prevent the sortie rate reaching a ridiculous figure, which might later prove an awkward operational requirement. They had made their point with crushing effectiveness, and it went a long way towards subduing criticism from the uninformed.

The Army dropped their Cheyenne helicopter program, and the Air Force went on to develop the AX into the A10 which was designed specifically to give close support to the Army. During the hearings on U.S.A.F. aircraft procurement, before the House Appropriations Committee, on May 21, 1969, Lt. General Marvin L. McNickle, Deputy Chief of Staff, Research and Development, compared the Harrier unfavorably to the AX, for which he was seeking funds. His criticisms of the Harrier were based principally on his contention that the British aircraft sacrificed too much of its mission capability to get vertical flight, as opposed to the conventional take-off and landing AX. In view of the vastly improved payload capacity of the advanced Harrier (AV-8B), it is interesting to read of the Air Force's commitment then, on the record, to the general concept of V/STOL.

Congressman Minshall who had just watched the Harrier demonstration in America, following the Transatlantic Air Race, said: "I am not an expert on this type of aircraft, but it was a very impressive demonstration from a layman's point of view. I wondered just what it would do under actual battle conditions?"

General McNickle said, "We would like to have an aircraft of this type that would have greater range and payload. We have had some people participating in the test program all along."

Brig. General William Pitts (Director of Budget) stated, "General McNickle has gone on record before the Senate and House Armed Services that the Air Force is desirous of having a plane with vertical takeoff and landing capability. But, as he said, at this point in time we have not reached the state of the art in engine development to give the range the Air Force needs to carry a proper bomb load to do a proper job." It will be interesting to see how long it takes the AV-8B to help them change their minds.

When the Marines burst upon the scene and decided to buy the Harrier, it could not have come at a better time for the aircraft's development. The first R.A.F. squadron was not actually formed until April 1969 and in 1967, just before the Marines came across, there was great gloom about the entire future of the Harrier. There was a real fear amongst Harrier Siddeley people that the R.A.F. requirement for the airplane would be withdrawn. There was a strong lobby within the Air Force, who were becoming excited about the proposed new Anglo-French swing wing attack aircraft, the AFVG, and they felt they should not proceed with this strange V/STOL concept. One of Hawker Siddeley's friends within the Ministry of Defense told them that it was a case of the few fighting against the many, and that if the program did survive, it would be due to the sheer determination of a handful of individuals. The Harrier somehow escaped the axe in that defense review, but it was yet another example of the tunnel vision the airplane had to combat in its own country of origin. Hawker Siddeley was so convinced at that time that it would be scrubbed that they started designing another airplane, the Hawk jet trainer.

Thus, if the Harrier had gone down in 1967, the Marines would never have gone to Farnborough Air Show. It also meant a boost for the production line at Kingston-on-Thames because at the time contract negotiations started, the intention was to have only sixty, and the whole tooling program was based on that. In fact, the R.A.F. did later go on to have almost twice that amount. It was a time of great pride and self-congratulation for the British planemakers. In American terms, they were a small aerospace company, but they succeeded where the might of the American aircraft industry had failed. Now, the Marines were to take the little airplane by the scruff of the neck and make it do things that amazed and delighted its designers. This was the beginning of a highly successful and happy partnership.

It seemed that the Harrier's luck had changed, but the makers never believed that it would change to the extent that it did. They were under no illusions about the sale to America. They anticipated that even if the Marines were allowed to buy the full 114 aircraft, then the best they could hope for was a lucrative license agreement under which the airplane would be manufactured in America. To their delight, though, they finished up manufacturing all of that first buy in England. It was certainly not the original intention of the politicians, as epitomized by Mr. Mendel Rivers, chairman of the House Armed Services Committee and his counsel Mr. Russ Blandford on May 5, 1969.

Mr. Blandford said, "I think in all fairness to Hawker Siddeley that somebody should tell them that if they think they're going to equip the Marine Corps and possibly later on the Navy with the Hawker Siddeley Harrier, to me this would be a pipedream. The Congress would never approve the purchase of a foreign made airplane for combat purposes."

General Chapman responded, "Mr. Blandford, we do have some indication that U.S. manufacturers have shown considerable interest in follow-on license agreements. There is nothing definite, but they have shown an interest."

Mr. Blandford added, later, "Mr. Chairman, I think it should be made clear, this committee I think has made it clear, through the Secretary of the Navy and others, that this is a one time buy from Hawker Siddeley and any future —I think this should be made clear on the record—will be through U.S. licensed companies."

Mr. Mendel Rivers stated, "I have told the Siddeley crowd, as far as I was concerned as one member of this committee, we considered nothing else that didn't have a consideration of a license to American manufacturers. We have a lot of people that can make that plane in this country. I can think of half a dozen right now. . . .

"I want to see this plane, which we have spent money

on to develop—and it has terrific promise—manufactured in America."

Well, that was pretty clear-cut, and there was no doubt they meant it. In the end, however, the first five years' procurement went to England for the simple reason that it was cheaper to build them there. Politically it was not very palatable, but the economic reality had to be swallowed. However, back in 1968, the reality of the situation seemed to be a shotgun marriage between Hawker Siddeley and an American manufacturer. Throughout 1969, the English company was courted by big aerospace companies like Grumman, Chance Vought and McDonnell Douglas, and eventually after much negotiation McDonnell won the license to manufacture the Harrier on the other side of the Atlantic.

It was to be a progressive changeover of production from Kingston in England to St. Louis in Missouri. The first year they would principally assemble components sent from England. The second year, they would have more tools and would start making their own components and so on, until at the end of five years they would be making the entire airframe. The theory was fine, and it would have meant the money being spent in the United States, but when the calculations were examined in detail, it just did not make sense financially. The premium was too high for making the tools and jigs and training the American personnel. Congress and Senate had to eat their words, and Britain's balance of payments got a most welcome boost.

The news of the Harrier was greeted with dismay by most Marine pilots. They were heavily involved in the Vietnam war at that time, and their main light attack aircraft was the Douglas A4 Skyhawk. It is no exaggeration to say that the Marine Corps aviators loved the Skyhawk. The aircraft was reliable, nice to fly, and it took an awful lot of punishment and still kept flying. Besides, they had 10,000 feet of concrete wherever they wanted to go, and with air superiority they were not going to lose these runways to enemy air attack. Therefore, an airplane that could take off straight up was hardly at the top of the list of priorities for those front line pilots. However, when they started to analyze what they could have done with the aircraft in Vietnam in terms of basing it closer to ground units for quick response to calls for air support, then the advantages became clear. The benefits were pointed up when they recalled that in 1966 the Marines had explored the possibility of putting in an expeditionary airfield at Dong Ha only twelve miles from the demilitarized zone. At that time, in 1966, their major combat planes were located about 100–150 miles from the DMZ, and the time of response was correspondingly longer to calls for firepower from ground units. The Harrier would have fit neatly into Dong Ha, without the expense and effort of a major expeditionary field, but the study at Dong Ha emphasized how interested the Marines were in improving their response time. If the United States had not withdrawn from that conflict when they did, or had reversed their decision to do so, then the Harriers would undoubtedly have operated there, and, as we'll see in a later chapter, the Marines think it would have proved the concept beyond any doubt.

The Harrier purchase was not motivated purely by the Vietnam war situation, but it certainly persuaded men of vision like General McCutcheon and Colonel Miller that V/STOL was the only way they were going to solve the problem of optimum quick response with any flexibility. The Vietnam experience had shown that most fights on the ground, throughout the five northern provinces, were resolved one way or the other in thirty minutes, so clearly quick response was vital. If the airpower was not overhead and hitting the enemy within that time, then it was virtually a waste of time. Aviation firepower accurately delivered can be far more devastating than conventional artillery. Each one of the load of 500 pound bombs which the Skyhawks were dropping was far more useful to the men on the ground than anything that could come out of the tube of a big gun. The Marines calculated that by using the Harrier in a Vietnam scenario, they could be hitting the enemy within ten minutes of the start of the ground battle. Swift, devastating and decisive —that's the whole thrust of the Marines' Harrier philosophy.

The American public is still getting used to the amazing flying qualities of the Harrier, and the reactions can be highly amusing. Major Drax Williams flew into Selfridge Air Force Base one day in 1976 during an open day. There were around 10,000 people waiting for three old Delta Dagger jet fighters to take off, for a fly past. The temptation was just too much for him. He broke into a tight turn over the field at around 500 knots pulling lots of G, dived straight at the ground and stuck the Harrier nozzles in the braking stop, and came to the hover at around 50 feet. The Delta Dagger pilots had shut down their engines and were running towards him. They had never seen an airplane do that before, and they were convinced it was about to crash. He pirouetted the aircraft towards them in the hover and dipped the nose in a bow. The leading pilot took off his helmet and bashed it on the ground. The Harrier could make show-offs of us all.

A Royal Air Force exchange pilot, Squadron Leader "Hoof" Proudfoot, led a flight of four into the Naval Air Station at Jacksonville in Florida in 1975 and they came to a stop in line hovering over the runway. "Hoof" would call, "Ninety right, go," and all four Harriers turned ninety degrees. People poured out of buildings, and traffic was backed up for several miles along the airfield perimeter roads.

Air traffic controllers have hit the crash button and sent out the fire tenders several times. Decelerating with a nose high attitude, the Harrier can give the impression of entering an approach stall. Air traffic people cannot get used to an airplane which comes into the final approach at around 180 knots and slows down to zero before landing. In bad weather, on a ground controlled approach, the controller was passing the usual information. About four miles out, the Harrier pilot gradually decelerated with nozzles, adding a little power to make up for reduced wing lift. That was fine. The controller had seen that sort of deceleration on radar before. On course, on glide slope and as the speed came steadily down to fifty knots, forty knots, the controller's voice started to fade. He knew the airplane had not crashed. He could see the blip on his screen, but it was not moving. "Harrier One. . . . Harrier One. . . . What the hell is happening . . .?"

Chapter 9

"The Most Effective All Round Fighter in Existence"

One of the most persuasive arguments for the Harrier concept is a story from the Indo-Pakistan war of 1971. Forty-eight hours after the start of hostilities an airfield at Dacca had been subjected to continuous, intensive air attacks. Despite the severity of the bombing, a squadron of Pakistani Super Sabre jets remained intact behind the protection of their concrete shelters. Yet, they never fired a shot in anger. They were completely written off simply because the runways had been cratered. The fact is that this could not happen to a Harrier. They could rise vertically from such a scene of devastation or even find a short stretch between the craters for a short takeoff with full bomb load. They can operate from forest clearing or obsolete military airfields. They can even be dispersed and hidden in places like factories or barns, to taxi out for takeoff from a nearby road. No other aircraft in the Western alliance has this capability to survive a first strike and come back fighting.

The Warsaw Pact has every single NATO airfield "pre-

A Harrier "goes to war" from a rolling vertical takeoff between the craters on a bombed runway.

targeted" either with missiles, or manned aircraft. Special anti-airfield weapons have been developed, and some Western observers are in no doubt that from the outset of any European conflict, the Warsaw Pact forces would use "all weapons" which means tactical nuclear warheads and chemical weapons. The use of such devastating power against runways makes it academic to discuss their repair. The airfields would be heavily defended with anti-aircraft missiles and guns, but an enemy would press home his attacks prepared to suffer heavy losses, for the prize is enormous. Deny an adversary his airpower, and chances of winning the land battle are dramatically increased. Each NATO airfield has its weaknesses catalogued by its potential enemies. Their pilots practice precise modes of attack on dummy NATO airfields which simulate every feature of the bases. Attack options are varied: high speed single pass low level attack with anti-runway bombs; bombing from high or medium altitude; air to surface missiles; short, medium or long range surface to surface missiles. They all carry the option of nuclear warheads, but assuming conventional warheads had been used, imagine the scenario after such preemptive strikes.

Airfield denial following heavy strikes. Harriers could continue to operate from this airfield in vertical takeoff, or using short takeoff with increased warload from short strips between craters on the concrete or across the grass.

The personnel who have not been injured will probably be demoralized by the attack, but decisions would have to be taken quickly to assess damage, and clear the rubble, and fill the craters. Any infilling of craters would have to be capable of taking the heavy wheel loading of contemporary combat aircraft, and this would involve a big effort in materials, equipment and men. All the time, there is the very real threat of a second strike designed to disrupt such work, plus the inevitability of delayed action bombs on the runways. However, it is not just big holes which leave a runway useless— a hole four or six inches deep could prevent a high performance aircraft from leaving the ground. Any aircraft in the air during the attack, short of fuel, and anxious to land, is in serious trouble, unless it can land vertically. Even if there is an undamaged strip between craters long enough for an attempted landing, it would require very fine judgment to put the wheels down immediately past a crater. In bad visibility, and perhaps with battle damage, this sort of short landing would be, to say the least, extremely difficult.

It might seem to most people that the Harrier must have been the aircraft the military all over the world had been waiting for. Now they were to be freed from the tyranny of fixed, vulnerable runways. Now, they were being offered this potent mix of flexibility, surprise and quick reaction. Life, as most of us know, isn't quite like that, and there are two principal reasons why the Harrier concept has had to fight so hard for acceptance.

One is that there has always been, and to some extent there still is, a very great vested interest in preserving the status quo. No Chief of Air Staff is readily going to concede that he had his head in the sand for years in pursuing policies which demanded conventional aircraft. Why, his political masters would ask, have you been demanding all this money for all these years and now tell us that at least some of the money could have been more wisely spent on this alternative? The wars in the Middle East and the Indian subcontinent did more than anything else to force such people to think hard about their longer term policies.

Another important reason is a myth which has persisted from the early days when the Pegasus engine was not fully developed. Many people then got the impression that the Harrier had a limited radius of action and was designed to perform its basic mission solely from a vertical takeoff. This is a myth that Harrier salesmen are still trying to correct. They do not present it as the universal panacea though. The Harrier is not all things to all men, but in the role for which it was designed, it is the most effective all around fighter in existence. The makers present it, in its land-based role, as a complement to conventional fixed wing airpower which, after all, does a splendid job, as long as the runways are available.

The Harrier might almost have been designed with the U.S. Marine Corps in mind. One of their primary missions is amphibious assault, and as we have discussed, airpower is a vital integral part of their armory. In the 1950's they developed transportable runways known as SATS (Short Airfield Tactical Support) which as the beachhead was opened out, would be laid for close support aircraft operation ashore. Fitted with a catapult and arrester gear, 2,200 feet of this metal planking could be in use by around the fourth day of an amphibious assault. Now, the Harrier has given the Marines the dramatic capability to get their airpower ashore much more quickly, and operate it very much closer to where the fighting is going on. In the initial phases of the assault, Harriers can operate from little helicopter assault ships, close to shore, without catapult or arrester gear. It is not surprising that the Marines have become so enthusiastic about the airplane.

During an amphibious assault the operations of the Harriers would be divided into three phases — operations

PHASE I - OPERATION FROM SEA BASE

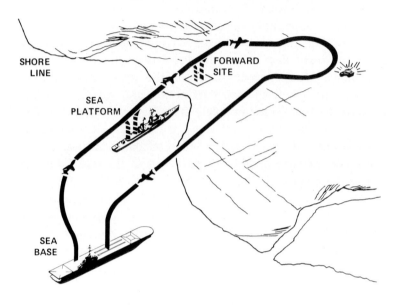

PHASE II - INITIAL OPERATIONS ASHORE

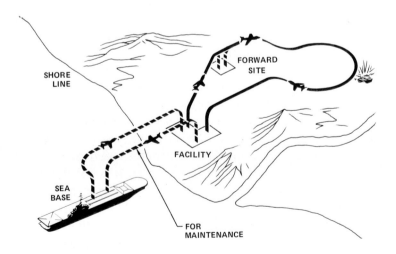

PHASE III - FULLY OPERATIONAL ASHORE

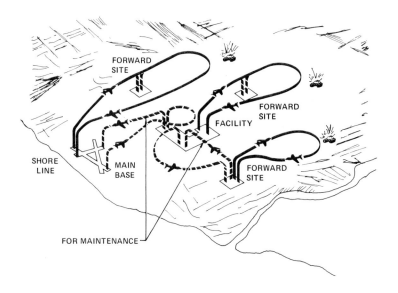

from a sea base, initial operations ashore, and full operations ashore.

The primary sea base is a small amphibious assault ship with a flight deck 600–800 feet long, and as the Marines showed during their trials on the U.S.S. *Guam*, in 1974, Harriers can operate very effectively in concert with helicopters from ships of that size. At the last count, there were twenty-one ships of this type in the Navy. Normally, these sea bases would be around fifty miles from shore and would be able to sustain air operations for long periods, including maintenance as well as refuelling and re-arming. So, as the first waves of Marines went ashore and started to fight their way inland, Harriers would have softened up the beachhead and would fly back and forth from the sea bases giving close support. Operating much closer to the shore would be some of the fifty-three ships the Navy has in its assault forces, which have a helicopter landing platform and which, therefore, makes them suitable "Harrier Carriers." Aircraft could either operate directly from these platforms since they would simply have fuel and weapons facilities, or they could be used as a staging post for aircraft from the main sea base further out. Either way, the response time to a call for air power obviously becomes less and less, the closer the aircraft are to the battle.

Before the advent of the Harrier, the only way to ensure quick response was to have aircraft constantly in the air, assuming air superiority, and to have them orbiting over the battle area. Then, when a ground commander called on the radio "come and hit 'em boys," the aircraft would descend, drop their ordnance, and then return to base. They would arm, refuel and get airborne again and loiter in the skies for the next call. It was a philosophy developed during World War II and was neatly named the cab rank. However, it is enormously unproductive in terms of efficiency and good utilization of resources. The Harrier flies cab rank missions as well, but it is a cab rank on the ground. The beachhead expands, the aircraft move ashore and start operating the cab rank, from a forward site.

As the troops move inland, they come across suitable areas for forward sites. These could be parts of a dock, a damaged runway, a parking lot, a forest clearing big enough to offer a landing surface at least 72 feet square. If the forward site is centered on something like a road which would allow short takeoff and, therefore, more ordnance carried, then so much the better. Frequently though, it would simply be a vertical takeoff and landing pad to which the Harriers would fly, loaded with bombs and fuel from the sea base or sea platform. The Marines have developed and refined the "spray-on" landing pad used by the tripartite squadron. Now a Marine with a device like a flamethrower can prepare

Harrier weapons potential. A selection of United Kingdom and United States ordnance.

a pad in a clearing in about twenty minutes, which will stand anything up to twenty-six landings.

Normally, a forward site could be operational within a few hours, but even in a lightly forested area less than twenty men would be sufficient to clear and flatten the surface for operation within a day. A typical forward site would have no maintenance or re-arming facilities in the early stages, simply a supply of demineralized water which the Harrier injects into its engine to improve takeoff characteristics. The pilot would fly from the ship, land on the pad, shut down his engine and "ground loiter," monitoring FM radio for a summons for airpower. The aircraft, probably loaded with 3,000 pounds of bombs, would lift off vertically, drop its ordnance and fly back to the ship for re-arming before returning to the cab rank at the forward site. Sitting fully armed at that site ten miles or so from the forward edge of the battle area he would only be a couple of minutes' flying time from the fighting on the ground.

The concept is based on the battle moving steadily inland, and as this happened, the next stage would be the setting up of a V/STOL facility which would be halfway towards the complete transfer of all the Marine light attack airpower ashore. The facility would be continuously manned, and capable of providing fuel, ordnance and limited maintenance for up to ten Harriers. Speed of construction is vital, so they would try to base it on part of a damaged airfield or a 600-foot strip of paved road, as a runway for short takeoffs and higher payloads. They might even upgrade a redundant forward site into a facility, but if that were not possible, all the 300-odd tons necessary can be flown in by helicopter to construct the facility from scratch. It would take about thirty sorties by heavy CH-53 helicopters, and the runways and taxiways would be laid out of metal matting. Depending on the difficulties, this could be completed between 24–72 hours. The facility would be located about fifty miles or 5–6 minutes flying time from the battle area and the cab rank situation would continue to operate.

The final phase would be the building of a main base ashore, an enlarged facility, at which major maintenance and support can be provided for a squadron of twenty, and from which fuel and ordnance would be ferried by helicopter or by road to the facility and to forward sites which it had been decided to stock to some extent. For major maintenance the CH-53D helicopter can airlift an empty Harrier in a radius of seventy-four miles back to main base.

For amphibious operation, where airfields do not exist or have been destroyed, the flexibility of the Marines' concept gives them a dramatically increased reaction time compared to the alternative of aircraft flying off a carrier which is forced to stay far out at sea surrounded by its antisubmarine protective screen. "Target decay," as the Marines call it, is the criterion which governs their close support philosophy. If a ground commander calls for a strike on the enemy, and the aircraft does not appear for half an hour or so, then he probably won the battle himself or has been overrun. Either way the target has "decayed."

On exercises like "Versatile Warrior," in 1972 the Marines were dropping bombs on targets twenty miles away, just over eleven minutes from the ground forces' request. Responsiveness depends on distance to the target, and no close support aircraft has better potential for this than the Harrier, as the Royal Air Force demonstrated in their exercise "Big Tee" in May 1974. During three 12-hour flying days, twelve Harriers flew 364 close support missions. The firepower that represented on target, was devastating — 1,100,000 pounds of bombs, plus 13,000 rockets, plus 77,000 rounds of 30 mm. gun ammunition. Although, in vertical takeoff, the Harrier's load is a lot less than some conventional attack aircraft, the VTOL aircraft's response and flexibility more than redresses the balance.

In operations from the forward sites, the Marine Harrier pilot sits in the cockpit monitoring the radio traffic between the Tactical Air Control Center and the Forward Air Controller up in the battle areas. Once he is given a mission, he will probably liaise directly on radio with the F.A.C. who gives him the map coordinates of the target, the elevation of the terrain, wind direction and the heading he should make his run on, so that he can pull up after the attack, over the friendly forces. The pilot reads back to the F.A.C. all the information, while at the same time he is going through his cockpit checks. Nozzles down, full throttle and he is off the pad and streaking towards the target at 450 knots. If it is a section of two Harriers, the wingman will have adopted a position about 2,000 feet behind at an angle of sixty degrees. This is the best position to protect his leader from air or ground attack. The F.A.C. will probably mark the reference point with a white phosphorous smoke grenade.

The Marines, of course, discarded the sophisticated INAS system because they felt its "warm-up" time on the ground took an unacceptably high margin away from their rate of response. If the attacks were being done with the Baseline system, which we looked at earlier, it would solve the bomb delivery problem with a computer using the information of airspeed and aircraft attitude. All the pilot has to do is superimpose a symbol on the head-up display over the target, and the bomb will hit it. It has an accuracy of around fourteen milliradians, which is good in the context that systems like INAS are around eight mils, and most fixed sight systems are around thirty mils. During an attack, the F.A.C. would be calling corrections from each bomb run and spreading the high explosive where it would be most effective. The aim is to have a bomb on target every thirty seconds. By the time the sound, the shrapnel or the heat from the napalm has begun to fade, and the enemy are putting their heads up again, there is another one. Even if the bombs are slightly off target, it is stopping the fire and giving the "friendlies" a chance to consolidate or even retreat. Ordnance expended, it is back for re-arming, refuelling and on to the cab rank again.

Lt. Colonel Jim Lary was one of the Marines' most experienced Skyhawk close support mission pilots during the Vietnam war, and his experience there has committed him to the V/STOL concept. Time and again, patrols of young Marines were ambushed, and the pilots flying close support learned that the toll of American dead and wounded tended to rise in direct relationship to the length of reaction time.

One incident bears examination in human and military terms, as an example of a mission where the Harrier could have saved lives. There was a U-shaped bowl about forty miles south of Da Nang which was commonly known as Antenna Valley. It was a natural place to get trapped, which is just what happened to a company of Marines who had been sent in there on a search and destroy mission. It was a fairly neutral area and although they expected to make contact with the enemy, they never expected the weight of opposition they ran into. They were outnumbered by five- or six-to-one and an urgent request went out for air support, from the forward air controller who went in with them.

Two Skyhawks led by Jim Lary scrambled from Chu Lai about twenty miles away, found the target easily, and dropped their standard ordnance of 500 pound bombs and napalm.

It was late afternoon, and by the time they landed again at Chu Lai, there was a further call for continued air support. There was a lot of demand on the Marine air resources that day, and there weren't any other aircraft available, so Lary and his wingman took off again for the valley. The time leaving the target to arriving overhead again had been forty-five minutes, and the situation was deteriorating. Darkness was falling, and the muzzle flashes from the guns on the ground showed that the forces had closed to about one hundred meters. It was a very challenging mission for the pilots. They had to run down over a 3,000 foot ridgeline into the valley, drop their bombs, and then pull up sharply over a ridge the same height on the opposite side. According to the F.A.C., they were dropping on target, and their firepower was having some effect, but there was such a strong enemy force that they just kept coming. The Skyhawks were gone for another forty-five minutes, and as they came back next time, they could see the muzzle flashes only fifty meters apart. Jim Lary asked the company commander on radio, "Do you really want those 500 pounders that close to you?" The officer on the ground pressed the transmit button and through the clamor of small arms fire and mortar explosions around him, he yelled back, "Let them go, or we're going to be overrun anyway." Then he stopped abruptly in mid-sentence. He was shot dead, and the next voice from the ground was his radio operator. The ground troops fired flares from their mortars, and in a hail of .50 caliber fire from the Viet Cong, the Skyhawks swept into the valley dropping their 500 pounders only thirty meters from their own men. As they pulled up from their last run and headed for Chu Lai, the radio operator on the ground told them their last sortie seemed to have reduced the numbers to about even. The badly mauled Marines withdrew from Antenna Valley with over 60 per cent casualties.

On a planned operation like that search and destroy mission, a section of perhaps four Harriers could have been attached to the company at the planning stage. The pilots would have been thoroughly briefed on the operation, the terrain, and the radius of action. In this particular instance, there was a very small airstrip actually in the vicinity which would have been ideal for vertical or even short takeoffs. Besides, even without that, they could have turned one of the hard surface local roads into a basis of a forward site and stocked it with sufficient ordnance for the sort of sortie they were envisaging. Their firepower would have been raining down on the enemy almost as soon as the Marines engaged them on the ground. Reaction time would have been almost literally within a minute from the pilot pressing the self-starter. They would hardly have lifted off from their forward site when they would have been rolling into the attack on the white phosphorous marker. With such short distances to fly and simply heaving new bombs on to the underwing pylons and refuelling, the turnaround would have meant a devastating rate of bombs on target. Jim Lary is convinced that in that scenario in Antenna Valley, the Harriers would have neutralized the enemy forces in a fraction of the time. He should know, having suffered the harrowing and frustrating experience of knowing that men on the ground were dying because his conventional close support aircraft could not get there quickly and often enough.

If a conventional war breaks out in Europe, the forces of the Warsaw Pact will strike across the North German plain in a massive armored thrust. The five Harrier squadrons of the Royal Air Force, based in Germany and England, are trained to kill tanks, and their primary mission, operating from dispersed sites, would be to hit this armor at the "choke points" in their main lines of communication. NATO believes its ground forces have the "organic" firepower to take on the leading tactical echelons of this armor, which means the role of the Harriers would be to go about twenty or thirty kilometers beyond the forward edge of the battle area and hammer the tank reinforcements which, if unimpeded, would be thrown into the battle within a few hours.

The Royal Air Force works on the premise, and say they're not being naively optimistic, that there will be a couple of days of buildup of tension to give them a chance to disperse their aircraft before any shooting starts. A considerable number of dispersed war sites within a few minutes' flying time of Gutersloh Air Base have been chosen, and within a few hours of a buildup of tension, the Harriers would fly out to these and their fuel and weapons and other support equipment would be transported to them. The bulk of the weapons would be stored in concealed logistics parks, a short distance from the actual flying sites, probably just far enough away to prevent any explosion following an attack on the dump, blowing up the airplanes as well.

There is no doubt at all that to operate the Harrier from dispersed sites means a big logistics operation. The entire Harrier force in war would be something around 2,000 men, including Army engineers and the Royal Air Force regiment who defend the dispersed sites against infiltration. There is a large number of vehicles involved, including a hydrant refuelling system which has to be laid. Critics who point to this

premium which must be paid, ignore the bonus this dispersed
operation provides to any commander: flexibility, surprise
and, most important, survivability. And never forget the
enormous logistics exercise involved in supporting a tank regiment. Armies have lived with that for years because of the
advantages armor gives them.

The logistics requirement for the Marine Corps' amphibious assaults is mindboggling, but as far as the aviation forces
are concerned, there is one salient point to remember. The
total amount of bombs required will depend on the tactical
situation, and the amount of fuel required will depend on the
aircraft delivering them and the time and distance involved in
delivery. Harriers, supporting amphibious landings, would
present much less of a resupply problem based close to the
action using "ground loiter" while waiting for missions. As
far as the Marines are concerned, the deciding factor is the
distribution network, and Harrier pilot Colonel Eugene
Russell has made a study of this, placing Harriers in a Vietnam war-type scenario.

In Vietnam, bombs and aviation fuel normally came by
ship to Da Nang, and from there were moved to air bases by
small ships or by road transport. Russell is convinced that
Harriers could easily have used the same network. Instead of
a one hundred truck convoy leaving Da Nang carrying fuel
and bombs south to Chu Lai, several smaller convoys would
have supplied a larger number of dispersed Harrier sites. However, his calculations indicate that the total supplies would
have been no greater. Colonel Russell, who is now commanding a Marine Air Group, would not base his operational philosophy on the necessity to resupply sites by helicopter. It is
an option, but he sees sites being stocked in the same way as
conventional airfields wherever possible.

The extra vehicles and equipment do pose an additional
headache— the problem of detection from the air. Camouflage is very important, and exercise sorties are frequently

flown against Harrier sites by reconnaissance aircraft. On most occasions, even if they have been told the area where the site is, aircraft using straightforward visual photography have had great difficulty. Infrared makes it easier, although on one exercise, not one of six sites was found during a complete day's flying. Heat sources which the infrared camera picks up are very difficult to disguise, so if the airplane with I.R. actually flies over your camouflaged site with his camera on, he will photograph it. However, actually coming back and successfully attacking it is another matter. Harrier pilots, actually flying from the sites, frequently have difficulty locating them for the first few sorties. In the event that a site was detected and the Harriers did not redeploy to another, they are so well hidden that an enemy pilot would have great problems acquiring the target visually. Tossing a bomb at random into a wood is not likely to be very effective.

There are three methods of operation which the Harrier force could adopt in wartime. If they were caught completely by surprise, before they could disperse from the main base, they would slog it out from there. Assuming their hardened "hangarettes" had protected them from destruction on the first strike, they would emerge with the other conventional aircraft on to an airfield whose runways are almost bound to have been bombed. If the enemy has done an effective job with their anti-runway weapons then it is unlikely that conventional aircraft could operate from there for many hours. The Harrier could take off immediately, either vertically or with a full weapon load from any undamaged 300 yard stretch of the runway.

The second possibility is to have the Harriers deployed during a period of rapid escalation just inside, or just outside the main base, using perimeter roads, grass strips and taxiways. This gives them limited dispersal and thus some protection from surprise attack, while offering the main base facilities as a major logistics park. This would give the Harriers the protective screen of the airfield defenses, including antiaircraft missiles during their operations.

The third option, which puts the aircraft in its natural environment, is full dispersal to the war sites. The Royal Air Force has found that the optimum number of aircraft to operate from each site is six. Their weapons payload from a short takeoff is around 4,000 pounds, plus 5,000 pounds of internal fuel. Their main anti-tank weapon is the BL 755 cluster bomb. They can carry five of these on the underwing and center line pylons, and each cluster bomb contains 147 tiny bomblets which are released from the main bomb casing when it is dropped. Dropped on tank parks or concentrations of armor on roads or bridges, it is a devastating weapon with a large "weapon imprint." Just one bomblet in the right place will kill a tank. They can also carry six pods of SNEB rockets, each pod containing nineteen rockets. That makes a total of 114 rockets in one load. There are also the two 30 mm. cannons under the fuselage, which are capable on their own of opening up lightly armored vehicles.

In war, the pilots would be unlikely to leave their cockpits until they had no weapons left, or they had been shot down. They would be "tele-briefed" in the aircraft while it was re-armed, and maps marked with targets for the next mission would be brought to them. There would be no shortage of targets. The only problem would be keeping up a sortie-rate fast enough to stem the tide of the Warsaw Pact's numerical superiority.

Apart from the interdiction sorties, hitting armor beyond the forward edge of the battle area, Harriers would also be flying search and destroy missions. It is likely that enemy armor would have punched holes in the front line and on that sort of mission the Harriers would be likely to be involved more in the Marines-type operation of close support to troops on the ground.

Another scenario is one where NATO forces might have

sucked a large number of tanks into what they call, for want of a better expression, a "killing zone." The Harrier's brand of quick response, flexible airpower could have a decisive effect on the outcome of that sort of entrapment. Flank assaults by MIL 24 Hind troop-carrying helicopter gunships are likely to be launched by the enemy to seize bridges and other crossing points for tanks. The Harrier force's control system through their Army ground liaison officers is designed to give them swift intelligence reports of this sort of assault, where rapid employment of airpower could again be vital.

In action, the Harrier squadrons' link with the progress of the land battle is through the army ground liaison officer (GLO) who is attached to each squadron and whose role is to "task" the aircraft for each sortie. I flew on a simulated combat mission with four Harriers of No. 1 Squadron based at R.A.F. Wittering in the Midlands of England. The target was a bridge in the North of the country with "armor" crossing. Our mission was to "attack and destroy" the tanks at this river crossing. The task sheet from the GLO contained a lot of information: formation call sign, grid references and map numbers for the target, time on target, position of "friendly forces," frequency and call sign of any forward air controller. Low flying is heavily restricted in England, and in the area of our sortie, there were several spots which were to be avoided because of noise or gliding activities. The R.A.F. takes advantage of this by pretending that these spots are SAM missile systems, and the task referred to these spots as such.

The formation leader got the relevant maps from the GLO clerk on a half million scale on which the flight to the target area would be navigated and then a fifty thousand scale on which the clerk had already plotted the target. The formation leader selected an initial point (IP) on the half mill map. The IP is a unique feature in the terrain around the target which the formation leader can easily navigate to before switching to the large scale map for the actual run in to the attack. We were to be attacking from the west, and he chose the only wood in the area as his IP. It was an ideal choice, as it was almost in a straight line to the target from the east, and it was easily recognizable because it was on a fairly steeply rising easterly slope. The formation leader drew lines on the map with headings and timings for the attack on the bridge and the other three pilots copied it on to their maps. Since the secondary role of the mission was to seek and destroy in a limited area to the southeast of the bridge, a second IP was chosen by the formation leader for that, and lines and headings were copied on to the maps. No weapons were actually to be fired on this mission, but the ordnance was a rocket pod on each of the outboard pylons and three cluster bomb units, one on each of the inboard and center line pylons.

The four Harriers flew a defensive battle formation. Red One and Three were in front, in line abreast, separated by about 2,500 yards. Red Two and Four were swept at about sixty degrees to the outside of their respective element leaders and 200 yards behind. I was in Red Four, the two-seat Harrier flown by Flight Lieutenant Pete "Bomber" Harris. We descended rapidly to 250 feet on a heading of 226 degrees. On the headup display was an airspeed of 420 knots. The square shaped wood of the IP flashed past on our port wing and the pilots clicked their stop watches on. Twenty-five seconds from the IP, Red Three and Four (our plane) rolled over the other two Harriers in a hard left turn. This is the start of the spacing for the attack, but the crossover was also a defensive move to allow Three and Four to clear the area behind for enemy fighters.

Thirty-five seconds from the IP, Red Leader pulled up to 1,200 feet, identified the bridge and rolled almost inverted as he tipped into his shallow dive on the bridge. His number two, who gave a fifteen second separation during the pull up, followed him down the dive. Flight Lieutenant

A Harrier GR1 of No. 1 (F) Squadron taxies from its hide on exercise in Scotland in 1971. This aircraft carries two 30 mm. gun pods with rocket pods and drop tanks.

Harris and Red Three, having cleared the area behind for fighters, reversed back on to the original heading. Red Leader and his number two had been sky-lined as they went down the dive, and all we had to do was assess where they were pointing, pull up and acquire the target. As we attacked, fifteen seconds after Red Three, to allow "bomb fragments" to settle, Red Leader who came off low from the target was looking back up the dive, clearing the area behind again for lurking enemy fighters. He then reversed back on to the attack direction, and defensive battle formation was formed again as we steered 124 degrees on the head-up display to the second initial point.

On the run in to the first target, the pilots checked that the weapons were fused "nose and tail" which told the computer that the weapons were to be bombs, not rockets. As they pulled up, they selected weapons aiming mode on the head-up display, which meant "flying down" the vertical line on the display until the symbol crossed the bridge, then pressing the release button on the stick top. The inertial navigation system had worked out allowance for wind. En route to the second IP, rocket pods were selected, green lights showed they were live, and a rocket aiming display appeared on the HUD.

Red Leader selected a relay station on a hilltop as a target of opportunity. As they flashed past at 250 feet, the Harrier pilots pressed a button on the INAS, flew on for about six miles then reversed, following the steering information on the HUD back to the target. At three and a half miles from the target, our pair again crossed over, heads swivelling behind to look for other aircraft. At three miles from the relay station, Red Leader and his wingman pulled up and reversed left looking for the target. The INAS had been giving the distance and bearing continuously, and now in the HUD it had computed the correct depression for rocket firing in the prevailing wind conditions. They put the aiming symbol on the target at a thousand yards and pressed the button.

The airspace of Europe, in any future war, would be a very hostile environment indeed, and the R.A.F. reckon that their best chance of surviving is to fly low. That means in action going right down as far as they can without actually flying into something. It is not only going to give them some protection against missiles, it also will make them very difficult to spot from the air as they hug the nap of the earth at around 500 miles an hour. They accept they would lose Harriers, both to SAM systems and to the Warsaw Pact's very efficient ZSU 234 antiaircraft guns which they have in very large numbers. However, if the enemy forces hope to achieve their objectives within a few days, they would have to move at great speed and that does not make for easy target acqui-

*A U.S. Marine Corps AV-8A Harrier firing air to ground
rockets in a dive attack at China Lake, California.*

sition with fire control radars as convoys push along roads.
The Marines have had to rethink their attitude towards
low level flying. In recent wars, they had air superiority
which gave them, at least in the early days in Vietnam, the
luxury of rolling in from 8,000 feet with lots of time to acquire the target and release weapons, before they came
within effective range of small arms fire. However, the mass
development of hand-held Strela-type, heat-seeking missiles,
which can be spread easily throughout the battlefield, has
introduced a whole new threat. The Marines' electronic
countermeasures system is not going to help against heat-
seekers, so they had to adopt a low level philosophy similar
to the Royal Air Force.

As part of their training for low level evasion of missiles,
Marine pilots have been flying against their own Hawk missile batteries and Redeye hand-held missiles. They found

Harrier in a low-level, high speed flight, nozzles aft, forming visible vapor in the high Mach number airflows over the wing and in the tip vortices. This was during John Farley's spectacular demo at Lugano, Switzerland, 1973.

that, with the right conditions of airspeed and altitude, it is extremely difficult, even for highly trained operators, to get enough tracking time to get off a good shot at a Harrier. The Harriers were coming in at 450 knots and treetop height, so even when they knew which direction they were coming from, the missile batteries' prospects of a kill turned out to be fairly low. The Harrier's jet efflux is virtually smokeless, which is another problem for any gunner trying to pick it up at a distance. It takes a lot of low flying training to go that low, and that fast, but the Marines are now concentrating on it.

No matter what way you look at it, airpower means taking a munitions load from one point to another and dropping it accurately. It doesn't matter what you do it with. The real argument is how to do it most effectively and efficiently. Does the advent of systems like the Cruise missile mean that the role of aircraft like the Harrier is redundant? Cruise missiles are pre-programmed and dependent on knowing exactly where they have to go. It may be possible in the future to transmit information via a surveillance satellite which would enable a Cruise missile to hit a moving target.

If that were to happen, it might supplant the role of some long range interdiction aircraft, but it would not solve

A section of U.S. Marine Corps AV-8A Harriers of VMA 513 (the first U.S.M.C. Squadron to form) in low-level, high speed pass on desert range targets at China Lake, California, 1972.

the problem of close support on the forward edge of the battle area. Right there, in the thick of it, when the shooting starts, nothing is going to replace the response and flexibility of the human factor. Nothing on the horizon offers the Harrier's ability to survive and come back fighting.

Chapter 10

Marines Discover Power of Thrust Vectoring: VIFF

Major Harry Blot, U.S. Marine Corps pilot and test pilot with 2,500 hours flight time on twenty-five different types, was based at the U.S. Naval Air Test Center at Patuxent River in 1969 when he was assigned to preliminary evaluation of the Harrier. His first flight was a depressing experience. The Harrier was the most demanding airplane he had ever flown. He did not like its rearward visibility, and it didn't turn fast enough. It also had another annoying feature. Whenever he put the jet nozzles down in forward flight, the nose would pitch up almost thirty degrees. He thought it was a nice attack aircraft, but as a fighter, forget it.

In 1971, Harry Blot was assigned to the newly-formed Harrier Squadron VMA 513 and made Project Officer in charge of thrust vectoring. The Marines cancelled two squadrons of F4 Phantoms to make room in their budget for the Harriers. Now, the pressure was on to prove that the new airplane could fight its way out of trouble in air combat, without fighter cover. Thrust vectoring, changing the direction of the Pegasus engine's thrust by swivelling the nozzles in flight, had already shown how dramatically it could decelerate the airplane. The Marines were convinced there was untapped potential in it, and on an early sortie Harry Blot rolled the wings in the direction of a turn, then put his nozzles down. That infuriating pitch-up of the nose now sent the Harrier into a rate of turn he'd never experienced before.

The Marines had discovered the power of VIFF. It is a technique which has given Harrier pilots immense confidence. In one-on-one dogfights, they have been "shooting down" aircraft like the F14 Tomcat. With VIFF, the Harrier pilot can accelerate and decelerate without throttle movement, increase his rate of turn, and fly at abnormally low speeds. No opponent can predict what his next move will be, which means a massive injection of one-upmanship in that vital psychological aspect of air combat.

The story of VIFF reveals the surprise and incredulity of the aircraft's own designers when the Marines told them of how they stretched the Harrier's flight envelope. One man, though, was quite unsurprised by the dramatic improvements in the aircraft's performance. For almost ten years, aircraft designer and engineer Dr. John Attinello had been virtually a lone voice proclaiming the potential of using an engine's thrust in flight for things other than propulsion. The work of the Marines and the parallel test flying by NASA's Langley Research Center were now producing results which effectively said "I told you so."

In the early 1950's, Attinello was a designer of U.S. Navy aircraft, tackling problems associated with landing and taking off from carriers. The design constraints of making an aircraft compact enough for the restricted elevator size while fighting the size increases that came from making it land at low speed, convinced him then of the sweeping benefits that V/STOL could bring to naval aviation. The first time he saw the Harrier, flying off the U.S.S. *Guam* in 1971, its unique "four poster" arrangement of two jet nozzles each side excited him. Here was the ideal vehicle to test and prove the integration of propulsion and aerodynamics to gain super performance. It was to be an uphill task.

Attinello first discussed his thoughts on thrust vectoring with Hawker Siddeley during an official V/STOL study visit in 1961. He was convinced from his calculations that the extra amount of lift from thrust vectoring would produce a significant improvement in maneuverability. However, his calculations were based on the early 1960 wind tunnel tests on the P1127 airplane by NASA, and Hawker's people then, and later, produced figures showing, to their satisfaction, that the best one could expect was an improvement in lift of perhaps half of a G. Now, most fighters are stressed for about seven G. Clearly, as far as they were concerned, Attinello's improvements could be achieved more cheaply and just as effectively by adding a few square feet of wing area. Back in 1961 Attinello did not feel quite confident enough of his own calculations to argue a convincing case.

It may seem almost bizarre that Hawker Siddeley, the airplane's designers, should have been so unimpressed about an inherent characteristic of their own machine, a characteristic which, with hindsight, was begging to be exploited. At the time, they were designing a ground attack/reconnaissance aircraft, not a pure, highly maneuverable fighter. In 1965, when the Royal Air Force was laying down its operational requirement, there was no funding available for special development of thrust vectoring in forward flight. Besides, they were planning to go to war low level in northwest Europe with top cover from Phantoms and Lightnings. Another important point is that although Hawker failed to develop this enormous bonus, it is a tribute to the beautiful simplicity of the Harrier concept that the Marines were able to unleash the latent performance.

Attinello's interest never flagged, and around 1967, as

the Vietnam war escalated, his work there for the Institute of Defense Analyses gave him renewed impetus. His boss in the Weapons System Evaluation Group, General A. J. Beck of the U.S.A.F., was closely interested in Attinello's theories on VIFF. He asked him to carry out a study, called "Project Red Baron," on the air combat maneuverability of American fighters there.

American pilots were flying high wing loading Phantoms against low wing loading MIGs. In some flight regimes, the high wing loading airplane had the advantage, and vice versa. Attinello decided it would be nice for a fighter pilot to have his cake and eat it too. This meant the high wing loading aircraft could engage the low wing loading plane whenever he chose to do so. This concept brought him straight back to VIFF. Wing loading is a major factor in an aircraft's maneuverability. In simple terms, it is the weight of the aircraft divided by the square footage of the wing. Low wing loading helps reduce the radius of a turn and also an aircraft's ability to pull sustained G's. The Harrier is a high wing loading airplane. It seemed to Attinello that using thrust vectoring in the high wing loading Harrier one could exploit the aircraft's characteristics to a point where one was approaching the ideal.

General Beck was impressed but he wanted to test the reactions of his own pilots who'd had a chance to fly the airplane. Colonel J. M. Broughton was assigned to check with one of the U.S.A.F. project pilots who had been flying the Kestrel in England. The memo which Colonel Broughton wrote in January 1968 detailed the alarming experience of a Lt. Colonel Campbell. This seemed to signal the end of VIFF as a serious contender for U.S. government funds. Remember that at this time, the Marines had not even expressed interest in the airplane.

The damning part of the memo read, "There have been some nozzle deflections in excess of the 180 knot restriction.

Lt. Colonel Campbell inadvertently activated the nozzles on downwind leg at 240 knots. Although he immediately noted his error and reactivated the nozzle control, the aircraft reacted violently. Control forces were severe and the deceleration was described as far in excess of speedbrake action. It threw him up against the windscreen and made control of the aircraft momentarily difficult. . . . The tests were abandoned due to the fear that the aircraft would be stressed beyond its structural capability. The maneuver is recommended for a desperation type situation only."

That memo blocked Attinello. People pointed to it and said that even if the forces he computed could provide the additional maneuverability, the horrendous control problems would make it unusable. Then, in the autumn of 1968, Attinello attended a briefing given by Tom Miller and Bud Baker on their first flights in the Harrier, the flights which convinced them the Marines should go all out for it. Attinello, like a dog with a bone, raised the memo with the then Colonel Miller. Well, had Tom Miller tried deflecting the nozzles in flight, and had he been thrown around the cockpit? Yes, he'd certainly done it. No, he'd remained firmly in his seat. According to Tom Miller, Dr. Attinello ran up to him and stopped just short of kissing him. He certainly wrung his hand! It was the clue Attinello needed to put together his official report of October 1969. That report led to the involvement of NASA, but, just as important, it made Colonel Bud Baker a disciple of the Attinello theories of thrust vectoring. When the Marines formed their first squadron, Bud Baker, the first Commanding Officer, made the exploration of VIFF a priority.

The Defense Department asked NASA Langley to review and comment on the Attinello report. They decided it had real promise, and a flight test program was worked out, using a Kestrel from the 1965 Tripartite Squadron trials which had been sitting unused in a hangar at Langley,

Virginia. Lee Person was assigned as Project Test Pilot and
Dick Culpepper as Project Engineer. Culpepper and Person
recall that Hawker Siddeley made discouraging noises. Putting the nozzles down at high speed, they said, could burst
the ducts leading to the reaction control "puffers" at wing
tips and tail. The engine, they said, could literally come
apart. There could be very serious handling problems, particularly at high angles of attack, directional instability. As
another pilot put it, "Faced with that sort of advice, that
test pilot was a real brave guy. He was really pushing the
frontiers."

The first part of the program was straight and level, conventional flying, with Lee Person aloft in the single seat
Kestrel and Dick Culpepper in radio contact on the ground.
They started off at 250 knots and changed airspeed by gradual increments. Hawker Siddeley's warnings were engraved on
Person's mind. He selected say 35–40 degrees of nozzle angle,
and started off with power well back, bringing it up slowly
until it got to just below the engine's maximum fan speed, at
ninety percent. His eyes concentrated on the duct pressure,
the angle of attack and the jet pipe temperature dials. To Lee
Person's delight, not to say relief, the airplane didn't come
apart around him. This was straight and level flight.

At around 300 knots and 15,000 feet he tried the
nozzles at thirty degrees, then forty-five degrees, the hover
stop, and right on through ninety degrees to the braking stop.
Contrary to the experience of the U.S.A.F. pilot, Lee Person
was not thrown around. In fact, it felt very good. He did find
that strong nose-up trim change any time the nozzles were
deflected down from the aft position, but it very quickly became a natural action to coordinate this nozzles-down position with forward stick to maintain the aircraft's attitude. At
nozzle angles of ninety degrees and beyond, the deceleration
effect was very much higher than anything he ever felt before. But, during this slamming deceleration, the negative G

straps on his thighs and the shoulder harness restrained him. It was very easy to visualize an enemy pilot over-shooting and presenting a target straight ahead. Encouraged, they expanded the flight envelope further. The next step was turning flight, maneuvering the airplane first without nozzle deflection, to get a baseline from which to work. Then they put the Kestrel into turns at various nozzle angles, holding the airspeed and measuring the forces and the accelerations they were getting. There was a really big improvement in turn rate. It was time to test it in combat maneuvers.

At around 450 knots, Person would throw the nozzles all the way down and roll the wings into the turn as the nose pitched up. This creates very rapid, very hard deceleration and hard turn. It brought the airplane into an area of very high angles of attack which Hawker had never encountered on the aircraft. It became a "cushion" turn. Suddenly, the pilot was pushing on the stick instead of pulling because it was wanting to pitch up so much. They ended up with thirty units of angle of attack on these hard break maneuvers. Did Hawker Siddeley have any strong feelings on that? Back came the reply, "You have more experience on this than we do." Both Rolls Royce and Hawker Siddeley reckoned, on paper, that the engine would surge or flame out at this angle of attack because it simply could not get enough air in. The NASA team proved it just was not so, and the engine and airframe designers were delighted to be proved wrong.

This initial exploration of VIFF lasted from January 16, 1970 to the end of June 1970. Person and Culpepper were overjoyed with the results so far. They just could not see any problems. Two things had clearly emerged. The tremendous deceleration capability, and the ability to maintain a constant turn rate with decreasing airspeed. The use of large amounts of nozzle deflection increased the aircraft's rate of turn while slowing it down. What was happening was that although the wing was losing lift, this was being compensated by the lift from the deflected engine thrust. Thus, in a turning dogfight when an opponent had reached the point of stall, the Harrier would still be turning tightly at ever decreasing speed and radius. When the enemy was forced to break out of the turn, the Harrier could reverse back towards him, throwing the nozzles aft and getting immediate maximum acceleration. Of course, the throttle setting had never been altered, and only the nozzle lever had been used. When the thrust was directed straight back again, there was no gradual build up. Acceleration was instantaneous.

No other aircraft in the world could do it. To a fighter pilot, it was almost a magical quality. As Lee Person put it, "I was enthused as hell." So, too, was the pilot of the highly maneuverable T38 aircraft which had now joined the program to simulate dogfight situations. Trying to follow the Kestrel through hard break maneuvers, the T38 pilot exclaimed one day, "Hey, you just made a square corner and you're coming right back at me!" The story was repeated on the ground and one of the experienced NASA test pilots refused to believe it. He flew the chase plane on the next sortie. After they landed, on the way back to the office, he grinned, "Do you know something? That airplane turns a square corner!"

The Kestrel, as the intermediate aircraft between prototype P1127 and fully fledged Harrier, had a limited wing and limited amount of thrust. So, although it was an ideal platform for proving the principles, it was clearly not as advanced as the Harrier in either airframe or engine. Even so, the Kestrel, using VIFF, did very well against the T38 whose wing loading was about the same as a MIG 21. Starting out in a defensive position each time, the Kestrel either managed to "draw," with no one getting the advantage, or it won outright. The advantages of the new techniques were spelled out during these dogfights. With VIFF, the Kestrel at the very least did not lose. Without VIFF, the simulated MIG 21 wiped it clean every time.

By this time, the Marine pilots of VMA 513 had started their exploration of VIFF. Although Project Officer Harry Blot was becoming firmly convinced of its benefits, the large majority of the other squadron pilots were still skeptical about its usefulness. It did not help its case when the flying qualities of a Harrier were fed into a computer and matched against other aircraft. The computer readout said the Harrier using VIFF could pick up perhaps half a G increase in turn rate, but the energy degradation associated with that made it look of dubious value. That just did not match with Blot's experience as a pilot, so the Marines persevered and put a pilot in a cockpit simulator linked with a computer. With a flesh and blood pilot "in the loop" the Harrier did very much better in these simulated combats than the earlier computer readout had predicted. Why this should have been true was puzzling. The next part of the actual flying program helped solve the mystery.

At Point Mugu, Harriers flew against Phantoms, Skyhawks and T38's, and, using VIFF, beat them. According to that computer analysis, Harriers should not have been able to stay in the sky with them. Most significantly, the airplane, using vectored thrust, was turning much more quickly than the designers said it could. Harry Blot telephoned Harrier Chief Designer, John Fozard, in England and told him the rate of turn they were achieving. "I've got a stopwatch, and I can pick out a spot on the ground, go all around a circle, come back to that spot, and click my watch. Alright, it's unsophisticated, but if my math is correct, I've just gone through 360 degrees in so many seconds and that's the turn rate, whichever way you cut it." John Fozard is not in business to knock his own airplane, but at first he could not believe it. The more the Marines flew his aircraft, the better they found it. Fozard may have been incredulous, but if one is going to have feedback from customers, how nice to be told your product is even better than claimed.

The Marines were now convinced, as their flight hours mounted up, that, properly flown, the Harrier should be able to beat any airplane in the sky in a dogfight. The facts they were documenting from this experience also revealed the basic flaw in the input which had produced the depressing results from the first computer tests. Certainly, it was true that thrust vectoring was only producing half a G extra lift, but the Marines discovered that a short burst of thrust vectoring took advantage of the tremendous pitch up to tighten their turns. Since they did not leave the nozzle deflected for too long, they were not losing the energy the computer said they would lose. They also made another significant discovery. If the pilot did it correctly, he entrapped the air on top of the wing, ending up with what they termed a "fully-blown" wing. That, said the Marines, was how they were turning circles faster than the designers believed the Harrier was aerodynamically capable of.

There were still quite serious engine limitations for VIFF, simply because no one had thought of using it in air combat before the Marines bought it. Now, they wanted these limitations lifted so they could keep their eyes out of the cockpit in a fight. They also felt the drive system for the nozzles needed strengthening. Rolls Royce and Hawker Siddeley agreed to modify all Marine Corps' Harriers on the production line.

Aggression and "press-on" are prerequisites of the successful Marine Corps attack pilot. They decided that VIFF was an essential tool in their fighting repertoire, and they were pushing on with a program which simply ignored the problems as if they did not exist. Rolls Royce, the makers of the Harrier's Pegasus engine, were aghast at one incident. For takeoff and landing, the engine has a rating which is higher than the nozzles aft rating. Nozzles aft, in conventional flight, the Pegasus puts out generally 16,000 pounds of thrust. The so-called normal lift rating, though, is about 20,000 pounds of thrust, a considerable difference for a little 16,000 pound airplane. This increase in rating is controlled by a sort of fuse, which screws in. The fuse is a jet pipe temperature limiter plug costing about eighty-five dollars. This takeoff and landing limit is restricted to two and one-half minutes. Well now, thought some bright Marine Corps aviator, just how long does the average dogfight last. Two and a half minutes! And wouldn't he love to get all that extra thrust in combat. The Marines came up with what they call the 675 plug which allows the engine to run at 675° C. jet pipe temperature, giving 19,000 pounds of thrust with the nozzles aft. They put it in a couple of Harriers and carried out flight testing. It worked. Then they formally asked Rolls Royce for clearance to use it on the engines of the entire Harrier fleet. The answer was an emphatic, "No." Rolls Royce went even further, "Do that to our engines, and we'll add a penalty to the contract." The Marine retort was crushing. They referred them to the last three engines Rolls Royce had stripped down for inspection. Surely Rolls Royce realized that those engines, which they reported in better condition than average, had been subjected to just this treatment? The Marines do not intend to use this extra thrust in everyday flying, but, in combat, engine wear and tear is of academic consideration.

As far as the Marine Corps was concerned, the contribution of NASA was invaluable in proving the VIFF concept. Marine Corps pilots were showing what VIFF could do for the Harrier. At the same time, Person and Culpepper were putting test and evaluation numbers on the maneuvers, making the Marines' assertions irrefutable. By this time, in June 1972, NASA was progressing towards flight tests of the only Harrier fully modified at that time for thrust vectoring.

NASA had exhausted the possibilities of the Kestrel by the end of 1970. If they were to pursue their pioneering work, they needed a Harrier. The problem was that the only Harriers potentially available at that time were the six development batch machines. These were aircraft set aside in England purely for development flying. They were specially instrumented for different aspects of performance, including navigation and attack, aerodynamics, weapon carriage, etc. John Attinello flew to England to try to arrange this for his NASA colleagues.

On the morning of October 10, 1970 at Hawker Siddeley's offices at Kingston upon Thames, near London, Attinello had a meeting with Ralph Hooper, Hawker's Chief Engineer, and John Fozard, the Chief Designer. Also present were Captain "Doc" Townsend, United States Navy, who was the fighter desk officer at Naval Air Systems Command, and then Colonel Noah New, who was the Marine Corps officer responsible for attack aircraft. New is now an admirer of Dr. Attinello's work. That day, though, he listened as John Fozard showed viewgraphs of calculations refuting Attinello's claims of greatly increased lift from thrust vectoring. What was said seemed to confirm New's conviction that thrust vectoring would be more useful for defensive than offensive maneuvers. The Harrier was, after all, being procured for close air support, and Colonel New told the meeting that the evaluation of thrust vectoring in flight was "not an immediate objective." As we now know, opinion on the value of thrust vectoring changed very rapidly amongst the decision makers in the Marine Corps, but at that time, Colonel New felt the Marines would not tolerate a delay in their program by diverting one of these six Harriers for NASA testing.

It seemed to be yet another setback. However, Colonel New's feelings on the matter were to some extent academic, for the control of the development batch was firmly in the hands of Air Commodore Eric Burchmore, Head of the

Harrier project for the Ministry of Defense and liaison man between U.S. and U.K. governments for the Marine Corps buy. Shortly thereafter, Burchmore was to meet a very influential friend of Lee Person. He was Neil Armstrong, the first man to walk on the moon. At that time, Armstrong was head of NASA's headquarters office, and he met Burchmore when he flew to England to discuss a number of joint programs, and to press NASA's case for a Harrier.

This posed a big problem for Burchmore, for the Marine Corps' buy of Harriers was officially supposed to be "off the shelf." Although there was clearly going to be a spinoff benefit to the Marines, the flying of the development aircraft was for R.A.F. purposes. Burchmore, with the support of the Royal Aircraft Establishment, detached the number two aircraft, XV 277, and ordered it to be modified for NASA. The R.A.F., which was giving VIFF a very low priority, was furious. Now, however, they are modifying all their Harriers to match the Marines' ability to vector throughout the flight envelope. At that time, Eric Burchmore's bold and farsighted decision made him an unpopular man in many quarters.

It had taken a great deal of perseverance, but NASA now had its Harrier. Armstrong then threw his considerable weight behind the idea of a joint U.K.–U.S. VIFF program between U.S.M.C. and NASA and the Royal Aircraft establishment at Bedford in England. This was signed in June 1972, and flying continued through until 1976. Yet, despite the results it was producing, the skepticism remained, even in the least expected quarters. Many people seemed to think that they were, quite literally, crazy. Person and Culpepper gave one briefing at the Institute of Defense Analysis in Washington, when some very senior, highly respected U.S. Air Force officers actually laughed out loud at their assertions. They were aviators of the old school who pointed to the Harrier's loss of energy when the nozzles went down. What they ignored was that fighter pilots had always given up energy in the hard break maneuver with thrust off, brakes out, trying to force an overshoot. They could not accept that the Harrier offered them that same capability, only magnified many times.

Both NASA and Marine Corps pilots were discovering that the more they pushed the Harrier, the more it continued to surprise them. Pilot after pilot has described it as "completely viceless." Pilots being what they are, they pushed it to its limit. According to one of the Marines' most respected pilots, they are still trying to reach that limit. "It's a pilot's airplane. It's way out and far beyond what Hawker Siddeley ever figured the airplane was going to be used for. You can wring it out until the airplane just won't do any more, but we don't know where that is. We always run across a lack of intestinal fortitude on the part of the pilot before we reach there. This airplane will do anything. It's just a fantastic airplane."

In Operation Battlecry at Point Mugu, Marine pilots flew against various aircraft including F4 Phantoms which were simulating MIG 21's. They were beginning to refine the VIFF procedures (Ill. 1). The Harrier always started off in

AIR COMBAT — TURNING

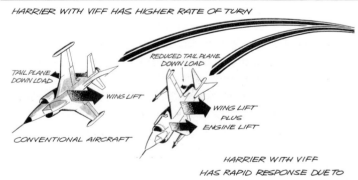

HARRIER WITH VIFF HAS HIGHER RATE OF TURN

TAIL PLANE DOWN LOAD

REDUCED TAIL PLANE DOWN LOAD

WING LIFT

WING LIFT PLUS ENGINE LIFT

CONVENTIONAL AIRCRAFT

HARRIER WITH VIFF HAS RAPID RESPONSE DUE TO PITCH-UP ON LOWERING NOZZLES

the defensive position with the "enemy" behind. It is an attack airplane and history showed they were most likely to start any air combat in this situation. That is fine because thrust vectoring was made for it. In a dogfight, the airplane which can turn just a little better is able to "track" the other and loose off some sort of weapon which will shoot the opponent out of the sky. Against the Phantom, the Harriers frequently shook them off simply by deflecting thrust and sliding to the inside of the circle. The Phantom pilot could not match the turn, and swiftly, as his arc became wider, he was faced with a dilemma. Should he try to tighten his turn or get out by banging open the throttle and zooming high? Phantom pilots swiftly discovered they could not live with Harriers in a tightening, decelerating turn. When they zoomed, however, the Harrier simply reversed out of his slow turn, banged the nozzles aft, and drove up behind the Phantom "like an elevator." When the Phantom pilot eventually committed himself, as he had to, and went downhill again, the Harrier flipped over with thrust vectoring and sat on his tail again. Very demoralizing.

Most Harrier pilots will try, in most situations, to win conventionally by staying fast. The reason is simple. They are better prepared, fighting at high speed, to counter any threat from another enemy who might happen along, or from their opponent's partner who is sitting up above just out of the fight waiting his chance. But, simulator experience has shown that even with the latest generation of high performance fighters, dogfights can degenerate in speed very quickly, right down to 120–150 knots, with the aircraft jockeying for advantage on the point of stall. There, the Harrier is in its element. Low wing loading airplanes normally revel in a low speed fight by forcing an opponent to go slow. When he goes past on the outside of the turn, they reverse on him, forcing him slower and slower until he is shot down. As the Phantom pilots discovered in Operation Battlecry, the high wing loading Harrier, using VIFF, is unbeatable at this tactic. A NASA pilot had great fun one day in the U.K./U.S. XV 277 program using this facility against an agile Hawker Hunter. The Harrier sat there, essentially in a hover, with just a tiny bit of forward speed. The red-faced Hunter pilot was running around him. Every time he tried to get away, the Harrier would point its missile at him.

VIFF has emerged as another potential dogfight winner in the "yoyo" (Ill. 2). In a level turn, at maximum power, the opponent's turn is resulting in a large radius. However, the Harrier pilot pulls up, squeezing his turn into a small radius at the top of the loop, by using his nozzles. He has now gained height, and therefore, more potential energy over his opponent as the nozzles pitch the Harrier quickly into the dive, pulling maximum G at the bottom of the dive and rolling to get closer to his opponent. Although he has accelerated quickly in the dive, he has done it without throttling back because, of course, he can reduce horizontal thrust with VIFF. The tremendous thrust to weight ratio of the aircraft is right

AIR COMBAT – THE 'YO-YO'

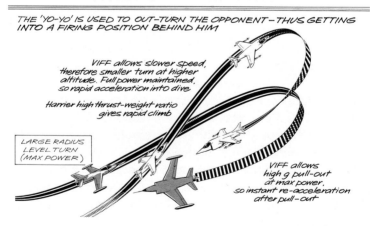

THE 'YO-YO' IS USED TO OUT-TURN THE OPPONENT – THUS GETTING INTO A FIRING POSITION BEHIND HIM

VIFF allows slower speed, therefore smaller turn at higher altitude. Full power maintained, so rapid acceleration into dive.

Harrier high thrust-weight ratio gives rapid climb

LARGE RADIUS LEVEL TURN (MAX POWER)

VIFF allows high g pull-out at max power, so instant re-acceleration after pull-out there, available, whenever he needs it. By then, he is right where he wants to be—behind the enemy.

Vietnam veterans flew through and survived the constantly escalating missile threat. In Vietnam, Marine pilots had a lot of different missiles fired at them, ranging from the large "telephone poles" down to the little hand-held Strelas. They saw the big ones a long way off, from their dust cloud on the ground at launch and sometimes from a white con trail behind. In the early days, the standard evasive maneuver was to roll towards it and dive down, then the SAM would turn to come after the plane. Once it had got its nose down, the pilot pulled hard up, and the SAM could not "hack" it. The enemy countered that by firing one high and one low. The answer to that was a barrel roll or some other maneuver that the missile could not follow with its stubby wings. Against hand-held infrared missiles which cannot be jammed, the tactic is to stay low and fast. Here, the Harrier pilot has an advantage denied to others. First, the exceptional maneuverability which VIFF gives you, and the fact that the nozzles are conveniently under the wing, which blanks out the plume of heat the missile's seeking. The Harrier pilot can turn towards the missile which no longer has anything to aim at. He can decelerate and turn so fast, the missile is going to get badly confused.

Vietnam veteran Major Drax Williams, U.S.M.C., thinks that Harriers flying at 450 knots, about 150 feet above the ground are not going to tempt too many pilots down into a fight. He recalled an exercise when he and his wingman were attacked from the rear quarter by a pair of simulated MIG 21's, diving down to try to lock on with heat seeking missiles. The "enemy" was forced down to low level in an effort to pick up the infrared plume from the confusion of heat signals thrown up from the ground. His wingman spotted the "bandits" at six o'clock about 8,000 feet behind and called "hard right." The wingman made a flat slicing turn at maximum G, using thrust vectoring to turn at around nineteen degrees per second. Drax Williams went straight up, initially giving the enemy fighters a planform view which blocked out his infrared sources. Nozzles at twenty degrees to get the initial pitch up, then over the top of the loop. He and his wingman were now separated in the vertical by about 2,000 feet, both pointing at the enemy. The bandits went for the high man, and Drax pointing down went into what is called a "dustoff" maneuver, flying straight at them. They pitched up and tried to barrel roll in behind him which presented a "shot" to Drax's wingman. Even Harrier pilots are fallible. He missed. Major Williams was left in a last-ditch situation with the enemy behind him.

It was time for the High-G Barrel Roll (Ill. 3). He tried to knock off every possible knot of airspeed to force a massive overshoot by his opponents. In a conventional fighter, he would have throttled back, put out his airbrakes and flaps, while rolling upwards through 360 degrees. But, he would have telegraphed his intention to the opponents the moment

AIR COMBAT — BREAK AND HIGH-G BARREL ROLL

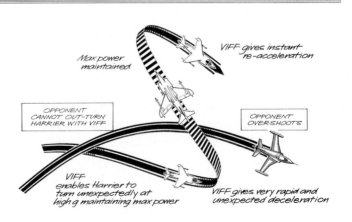

the flaps went down. Without touching the throttle, he slammed the nozzles down to sixty degrees, and the nose pitched up fifty degrees. He stood on the rudder and rolled, decelerating at about fifty knots per second. Going over the top he was down to about eighty knots as the enemy streaked past below. His nozzles aft, with instant thrust, he was in pursuit.

The skill of the pilot determines how well the Harrier is going to perform in air combat. VIFF alone is not going to save his life, which is why the Marines, and increasingly the Royal Air Force in Germany, spend so much of their time practicing the techniques. However, the Harrier pilot has an advantage denied to any opponent. The enemy can never predict what the Harrier is going to do next, because it does not rely only on normal aerodynamic forces. In combat, successful pilots see the continually changing scene, and subconsciously compute the projected flight position of the enemy. Nevertheless, this relies on previous experience of the combat behavior of conventional aircraft. The Harrier will rarely follow this mental forecast of a flight path so it drains an opponent's confidence. VIFF has confronted the enemy with a profound psychological disadvantage—the unknown.

Chapter 11

Engine Problems and Solutions

The Pegasus engine powering the present Harrier has the same basic layout as the BE 53 engine which first ran on the bench back in 1959. The difference in output, though, tells the story of the intensive development. That first engine produced only 9,000 pounds of thrust compared to the 21,500 pounds of the present day, and a problem which the engine people have constantly had to combat has been vibration. When the Pegasus was designed, it had the biggest fan that had ever been built. On the first bench test vibration gauges were fitted to the blades, and at 80 per cent r.p.m., the testing had to stop because of the enormous vibration on the second stage fan blades.

To the uninitiated, one aircraft engine is pretty much like the next, but every new engine has its specific problems. Bristol discovered that the vibration was being caused by the division of the flow into the two front nozzles, and to prevent the blades shattering, they increased the length from the nozzles to the blades and screwed tie rods between each blade. These were later replaced with platforms or snubbers between the blades which fitted into each other. It was a bit tough on the engine makers, for if they had been dealing with an aircraft like the Phantom with a long air intake, their job would have been much easier. The short P1127 intake, another constraint of the airframe wrapped around the Pegasus, did not give the air time to "get sorted out" before it reached those very long fan blades, and the air was badly distributed. The snubbers damped the blades so that this airflow did not set up frequencies of vibration which would break them. Sir Sydney Camm and his team wanted the lightest intake possible in their battle to keep weight down, and Stanley Hooker and his engineers accepted this and modified their engine.

Some of the earlier P1127 flying was done with an intriguing inflatable intake lip which was an attempt to strike a compromise between high speed flight when they wanted a fairly sharp intake lip for minimum drag, and a more bulbous intake for hovering. The inflatable intake lip was blown up to a bulbous profile for high intake efficiency at low speed, and then whenever the undercarriage was retracted, the rubber bag automatically sucked down to a sharper profile. The theory was good, and in practice, too, it worked very well, some of the time. After takeoff in some cases though, the bag would not suck down properly, and as speed increased, it flapped around and tore away. The death knell of the inflatable lip was just before the P1127 developed into the Harrier forerunner, the Kestrel. Two aircraft took off from opposite sides of the airfield, one with the inflatable lips and the other with a compromise metal intake. The aircraft with the fixed all-metal lips lifted off at a higher weight than the other.

One of the features pioneered on the Pegasus engine was contra-rotation of the two main rotating assemblies, the high pressure and low pressure spools. Had both these spools been allowed to rotate in the same direction, then it could have resulted in unpleasant "gyroscopic coupling" effects which would have unbalanced the aircraft's handling, particularly in the hover. This development was, in fact, initiated by the aircraft designers, but it was just one example of the cross-flow of development ideas which resulted from the close interdependency of the two companies over the years. It was a relationship which often resulted in considerable intellectual "gyro-coupling!"

One area of contention was the old enemy, the thrust center. John Fozard, faced with the problems of reconciling conventional and vertical modes of flight, used to sit across the table from Pegasus engineer John Dale and urge that the thrust center be moved further forward. Dale's argument was that if it were too far forward, then in some modes of short takeoff, it could cause pitching up which the pilot would not be able to control. The problem was this. The actual engine could not be moved forward because of the very short intakes. All you could do was to alter the thrust center by opening up the front nozzle area, and allowing more air to be pushed out through them. This meant that the engine tended to lose thrust overall, because the total thrust was constrained by the amount of gas coming out of the back nozzles. It is a constraint with which the normal engine designer does not have to cope. With the Pegasus, any attempt to uprate the engine thrust, meant intense thought on this balance between the cold air being pushed out of the front nozzles and the hot gas out of the back pair.

Despite the problems, though, more thrust was continuously being provided. The first P1127 hovering was done with a Pegasus 2 at a rating of 11,200 pounds, and this was rapidly increased to 13,500 pounds with the Pegasus 3. John Dale was always very reluctant to uprate an engine until he was absolutely certain he could sustain it. His boss, Stanley Hooker, constantly urged him to produce more thrust, and never mind what it did to the engine. Dale replied, "I'm going to look an awful fool if the pilot gets off the ground, and the engine breaks." Sir Stanley boomed, "You'll look an even bigger fool if the pilot opens his throttle, and it doesn't even take off."

Two stories illustrate the skill of the engine designers in coping with the unexpected. On November 30, 1962, test pilot Hugh Merewether was flying a wing development sortie in a P1127 from Dunsfold, measuring flutter damping. In a high-G turn in rain cloud at about 3,000 feet, there was a loud bang from the engine. It was obvious the engine had broken up, and then fire started in the engine bay. Despite the thick cloud Merewether, in a superb display of cool flying, managed to locate the airfield at Tangmere, and without any power at all, made a deadstick landing on the grass and walked away unhurt. His bravery and professionalism in saving the aircraft earned him an Order of the British Empire and enabled the engine makers to examine the Pegasus.

They made a fascinating and very significant discovery. The industry as a whole learned that day that the "fabulous" material, titanium, which had revolutionized engine design and development, also had its adverse qualities. The damage had been caused by a titanium fire in the rear stages of the high pressure compressor. The titanium blades had been rubbing against the casing and had not been able to conduct away the resultant heat. The result was fire and explosion. Bristol thought they had solved the problem by cutting a bit off the blades and increasing the clearances generally to prevent any blade contact, but the first time they put the modified engine in an aircraft, it surged and was impossible to fly.

This was an incident which illustrated the brilliance of Stanley Hooker. Where the others were baffled by the failure of their remedy, Sir Stanley took one look at it, and quite intuitively, without resorting to a single calculation, told them to make a few simple changes. To no one's surprise, it then worked perfectly.

The other, more recent incident, was of much more

concern to the engine designers. In April 1975, after nearly fifteen years and 100,000 Pegasus flight hours, an R.A.F. Harrier had a complete thrust failure during a climb to 30,000 feet. The pilot made every effort to relight the engine but was forced at low altitude to eject. The Harrier was completely wrecked, and a very battered Pegasus was brought by road to the Bristol factory. At the very center of the engine they found broken a bevel gear which drives all the engine and aircraft accessories including the fuel pump. It was hardly surprising the engine had failed. It seemed that metal fatigue, caused by vibration, had caused the failure. Tiny strain gauges, which detect bending in a component, were cemented to the rim of the bevel on a test engine and attached to electrical recording equipment. The bevel was rotated at 15,000 revolutions per minute as in flight and at the second attempt, on a test bed engine, very high vibration stresses were detected towards the top of the engine power range. Stress levels in excess of ten tons per square inch were measured as the vibrations rippled along the rim of the gear.

It seemed they had found the source, and they were convinced it was a "one off" problem. They were wrong. Just as they were analyzing this data, a U.S. Marine Corps Harrier crashed from the same cause. It was a harrowing experience for the men who designed the engine, to have a vital component start cracking up after such a long, successful run. While they tackled this problem, with the highest priority, all Harriers were temporarily grounded. For front line military aircraft, this was simply unacceptable, so the engine makers defined a band of engine speeds which were critical to the problem. Unfortunately, the critical engine speeds for each engine were different, due to small differences in the dimension of each bevel gear. A delicate probe was developed which could be inserted in a stationary engine to "excite" the bevel gear and determine its critical frequency, and this measurement was carried out in *every* Harrier. The Royal Air

Force accepted the engine maker's advice and flew, avoiding the destructive speed ranges. The Marines decided that two failures in 100,000 hours made the odds acceptable, and in typical fashion, they pressed on.

In the same way as a finger pressing against a bell stops it ringing, the designers clamped a damping plate to the bevel gear with a force of a thousand pounds. This virtually kills all vibration before it can build up. Rolls Royce had given it the highest priority, and seven and a half months after the R.A.F. Harrier crashed, they started delivering modified engines.

The Harrier is frequently flown at very low level and with these large gaping intakes there is a problem of bird strikes in the engine. An R.A.F. pilot at low level in 1972 was hit by several birds, and the engine lost all thrust. He tried a relight, failed, and successfully ejected. To his horror and embarrassment, as he floated to earth the mighty Pegasus roared into life, and the Harrier soared off into the wide blue yonder. It flew on, pilotless, for about thirty-five minutes at high altitude towards the East German border before it ran out of fuel and crashed. That pilot is said to have spent many hours pondering the exact wording of his accident report.

Chapter 12

Sea Harrier Defies the Wind

When Bill Bedford lifted off from the snowbound runway at Dunsfold that morning in February 1963, to rendezvous with the aircraft carrier H.M.S. *Ark Royal,* the most gifted visionary could not have predicted that he was taking the first step towards a revolution in airpower at sea. That first deck landing by a V/STOL aircraft effectively sounded the death knell of the big aircraft carrier, as we know it. The Harrier has turned virtually every medium-sized ship into a potential aircraft carrier.

Until the advent of the Harrier, there was no halfway house between the large carrier and the "helicopter-only" ship. Helicopters do a splendid job in their own defined roles of anti-submarine warfare and shore assault, but they have no capability to intercept fast aircraft or shadowers at 30,000 feet with "standoff" weapons. Up until now, large carriers were needed to provide a floating platform for fixed-wing airpower. The large size of these carriers has been dictated not by launch requirements but by the length of deck necessary for recovery. Even with modern arrester gear, decks still have to be fairly long in order to dissipate the tremendous speed on touchdown. The weight penalty would be too high a price to pay to make a conventional jet strong enough to withstand the deceleration of being stopped by a wire on a shorter deck. Therefore, the size of the conventional aircraft carrier is dictated by the landing speed of its conventional jets. Then, having built such a large platform, a navy is pulled into a vicious circle of putting a large amount of aircraft on to it to make it cost-effective.

The opposite is true of a ship operating V/STOL aircraft. They land vertically, so the ship is "sized" according to the takeoff run. Later, we'll look at the other operational advantages of the small carrier with Harrier-type aircraft, but for the moment let's consider one basic, compelling reason for their seeming inevitability—they are cheaper. The U.S. Navy has fourteen large aircraft carriers, at a current cost of around two billion dollars to build, plus the same again for the 100 or so aircraft on board. They are very efficient weapons, but you can build several mini-carriers for the price of only one present day carrier. Despite the enormous outlay on equipment and crew, no more than ten of these fourteen are available for sea at any one time. With the vast areas of ocean which the U.S. Navy would seek to control, aircraft dispersed on a much larger number of carriers would show the flag over a wider area. They would be able, for example, to offer more protection to convoys of vital supplies. There is another important point; the available eggs—the aircraft for strike and interception—would be spread around more baskets, making the carrier force less vulnerable. The big flat top is a large and tempting target.

It is an intriguing thought that, if it were not for the cancellation of the V/STOL P1154 project, Britain's Royal Navy would have been flying a supersonic vertical takeoff and landing fighter by the late 60's. The Royal Navy's last new carrier project was cancelled in the mid-60's, and the Fleet Air Arm had been declining towards an all helicopter force. Now, its fixed wing role has been given an exciting new lease of life in the form of the Sea Harrier, which entered service in 1979 and was the biggest single factor in Britain's victorious Falklands campaign. Its real importance is that it has advanced the state of the art beyond that of the Harrier into the first purpose-built maritime V/STOL aircraft. That is, if you discount the Forger. Even if a Western navy is willing to buy it and the Russians are willing to sell it, the question is, would it really be suitable? We shall look at this question again later.

The changes made to Sea Harrier *vis-à-vis* R.A.F./ U.S.M.C. aircraft were those considered absolutely essential for the Royal Navy operational requirement. The airframe and engine are 90 per cent the same as the land-based Harrier, while the navigation and attack system are about 90 per cent new. The biggest external difference is the cockpit, which has been raised eleven inches. This not only solved the problem of finding space for the extra equipment required in the naval version. It also greatly improves the visibility forward, downward and, most important for the fighter pilot, rearwards. The longer nose houses the Ferranti Blue Fox radar. Blue Fox is derived from the Seaspray radar used in the Royal Navy's Lynx helicopter, but greatly modified for the Sea Harrier's air to air, and air to surface roles, in which it will seek out and evaluate enemy aircraft and ships in all weather.

Sea Harrier's designation is FRS—fighter, reconnaissance and strike. In its fighter role it carries two 30 mm. guns and sidewinder air-to-air missiles. From its ship, its radius of action is up to 400 nautical miles and its potential targets are large subsonic maritime patrol aircraft and other attack aircraft threatening the fleet. In its recce role the Harrier in an hour's flight at low level can survey a staggering 20,000 square miles of sea, using its sophisticated surveillance equipment.

The Sea Harrier is about to undergo a "mid-life update" which includes adding to the wingtip area. This will enable two Sidewinder air-to-air missiles to be mounted on each single outboard pylon and will also enable the aircraft to turn a little tighter. An even bigger wing would help the turning performance even more, but there would then be difficulties because of the need to fold the wing for the lifts on the carrier. Leading edge root extensions (LERX) will also appear—they generate lift at high angles of attack and aid maneuvring— and 190 gallon combat tanks will increase the time on combat air patrol. The first live firings of Sea Eagle, the Sea Harrier's anti-shipping missile, have taken place. This missile is the equivalent of an Exocet, but with more "brain"—it has the ability to be more discriminating about targets, after launch.

But of all the equipment, the piece most ripe for replacement is the existing Blue Fox radar. It's a standard monopulse radar which works on the original principles of transmitted pulses being reflected back off a target. The time it takes for the transmission, determines the distance, and a blip is formed on the screen. The problem is that pilots are only interested in specific targets—ships and other aircraft. They're not interested in "ground returns" or reflections from an island. They require information on their radar about moving targets, and only a pulse doppler radar will supply it. The Sea Harrier's will be a derivative of a new Ferranti radar known as Blue Falcon.

It has a computer which looks at the objects confusing the issue and deduces that most of the objects being reflected are moving at the same speed as the aircraft, and can therefore be ignored. It cancels all that information and leaves on the radar tube only blips that have relative motion other than the aircraft's basic speed. It's also known as a look-down, shoot-down radar, and it will greatly increase the Sea Harrier's ability to identify and attack low, fast moving aircraft.

Another part of the mid-life update which will combine

with the Blue Falcon-type radar to make Sea Harrier a truly all-weather day and night interceptor, is AMRAAM (advanced medium range air-to-air missile). It will have a range in excess of 20 miles, and the weapons-aiming computer in the aircraft is being developed in parallel, to enhance its ability to intercept targets.

The Falklands crisis not only proved the Sea Harrier's devastating effectiveness in combat, it also indicated the important role which merchant ships could fulfil as Harrier Carriers, in any future conflicts. Within a few days of the outbreak of hostilities in the South Atlantic, the Cunard container ship *Atlantic Conveyor* was converted to a "garage" to transport Harriers and helicopters to the combat zone. Eight Sea Harriers and six Royal Air Force GRMk3's flew to Ascension Island and were then flown and vertically landed on *Atlantic Conveyor* at anchor offshore. On reaching the Falklands, the fighters were flown to the carriers. Only one Chinook managed to take off from the container ship before she was struck by Exocet missiles. In all, over 40 per cent of the combat aircraft used in the campaign, were ferried south in adapted merchant ships.

There had been no time to install Fairey Engineering's Medium Girder Bridge equipment as temporary ski jumps, but British Aerospace were sufficiently impressed by the limited use of this unique tactical option, to conduct a study of a Shipborne Containerized Air Defence System (SCADS). The basic concept is to provide a sea-going weapons platform to form part of a task force or a merchant convoy, in order to provide long-range defence against enemy air, missile or surface threats. This is a role traditionally provided by conventional aircraft carriers, but this is now prohibitively expensive for most countries. And, even for those who can contemplate this sort of expenditure, SCADS could be a cheap and effective means of radically altering and expanding their sea defence capability, by performing many of the roles of the vastly more expensive large aircraft carriers.

The Sea Harrier is of course the centerpiece of SCADS. Virtually all the other elements are containerized and, provided there is some advance provisioning, an ordinary container ship can be fitted with all the equipment to convert it to an aircraft carrier, in only 48 hours. Merchant container ships have a long, uninterrupted length of forward deck on which a Medium Girder Bridge Ski Jump ramp, manufactured by Fairey Engineering would be fitted. The runway would be 400 feet long and 45 feet wide and the ski jump exit angle would probably be 12 degrees, depending on the particular ship.

A merchant ship requires a highly efficient self-defense system, and this would be provided by a combination of the Plessey Shield passive decoy system, and the British Aerospace Seawolf anti-missile missile. Shield needs minimal maintenance, and deploys chaff and infra-red decoys to confuse and "seduce" incoming missiles, both diving and sea-skimming. SCADS also includes surveillance and air traffic control radar, a command center, and full support facilities. All can be lifted on to the ship in their containers. And there's an additional bonus—the containerization means that the equipment can also be used in a military role ashore.

A typical SCADS ship would carry six Sea Harriers and two Sea King helicopters—used in this role for airborne early warning. The support facilities include a hanger for two of the Sea Harriers and a Sea King; a full range of workshops for servicing and a fuel "farm" to support Harriers and helicopters for 50 flight hours per aircraft. The air group would have a complement of 31 officers and 159 ratings, and these "add-on" facilities would be self-contained and capable of operating for 30 days without replenishment. The total number of containers required would be 233.

Another fascinating concept being developed within existing technology could give Sea Harriers a unique ability to operate from small ships in very hostile weather conditions, and give these aircraft the capability to carry out missions which would otherwise be impossible. It's the SkyHook system which captures the hovering aircraft on the end of a crane and swings it on to the deck, then reverses the procedure to launch it again. It should mean that Harriers can operate from small ships in sea state 6 conditions, and the designers—British Aerospace and Dowty Boulton Paul—calculate that SkyHook would enable air operations from a 4,000 ton ship for 99 per cent of the time at sea, world-wide. It would also reduce pilot workload and make launch and recovery safer and simpler. The crane of SkyHook has a lock-on mechanism which engages a pick-up probe on the upper part of the mid fuselage. A SkyHook can be operated from both sides of the ship, simultaneously. The lock-on mechanism is space-stabilized, using a combination of inertial systems, computers and triple redundant control techniques derived from aircraft systems. This system allows the ship considerable sea motion, while managing to provide a stable platform for the capture or launch to be achieved.

The SkyHook is extended from its stowed position above the deck, ready to receive the Harrier, whose pilot commences a decelerating transition into the hover, aiming to come alongside the ship. To position the aircraft in the correct place for lock-on, the pilot formates on his hover sight. This is attached to, and shares, the crane's space-stabilization, and the pilot must maneuver within a 10 feet × 10 feet × 10 feet "window" to achieve lock-on. When he is correctly positioned, the SkyHook optical system acquires the aircraft, measuring both angle and distance to the pick-up probe, and the lock-on jack is then automatically guided by robotic techniques on to the probe. The lock-on is indicated to the pilot by a series of lights, and he then reduces power while continuing to control the aircraft in all three axes. The lock-on jack then pulls the aircraft up on to the docking pads which secure it rigidly. If the aircraft is only to be refueled, then the pilot allows the engine to idle. He shuts the engine down if he is to be swung on to deck for re-arming too. The SkyHook lowers the Harrier on to a trestle, it is secured in the hangar below decks, electrical supplies reconnected, and re-arming takes place.

The system is designed to launch and recover aircraft in the minimum of time. The designers caculate that four aircraft can be launched in less than two minutes from two SkyHooks. It should take around two minutes from the start of the hover, to recover an aircraft and secure it below deck. If re-fueling only is required, then this should only take five minutes for a typical Harrier sortie fuel load. A complete weapons turn-round should be achievable in less than ten minutes, and an extremely high sortie rate should be generated, because of the freedom from the normal constraints of waiting in line for other aircraft to clear the complicated deck-cycle of launch and recovery.

On a conventional aircraft carrier, the physical act of maneuvring aircraft for servicing and re-arming can be extremely labour intensive, very restrictive in terms of safety and operationally very demanding in heavy sea states. Mechanical handling by SkyHook would be very important in manpower and space, particularly on a small ship in heavy seas. Lowering a Harrier on to a trestle below deck enables it to be moved easily and very accurately to its parking position. This allows many more aircraft to be parked in the confined space below.

To re-launch, the SkyHook dips into the hangar, locks on to the Harrier and the trestle releases the aircraft which is lifted clear of the hangar. It is swung over the side of the ship, firmly in the grip of the crane, and the pilot starts the engine. The pilot receives his mission "tele-brief" through his radio and completes his cockpit checks. Nozzles are pointed down to control the aircraft as the lock-on jack extends downwards, clear of the docking pads. This takes around ten seconds, and when the green lights flash the pilot can slowly open up to full power. As soon as the lock-on jack senses the upward movement caused by the thrust of the Pegasus engine, it releases the aircraft completely. The aircraft is now in a free air hover, ready to move sideways, using the reaction control system, and then make the transition from the hover to conventional wing-borne flight.

Apart from the other advantages already discussed SkyHook will also mean an improvement in vertical take off and landing due to the avoidance of ground effect and hot gas re-circulation. And it will mean less fuel used for launch and recovery too. SkyHook could even be spread throughout a task force or convoy of ships simply as a means of re-fueling Harriers operating at long range from their "mother" ships.

The Sea Harrier has a unique ability to defy one of the elements which has dominated pilots since aircraft first flew from ships—the wind. From the earliest days of warfare at sea in sailing ships, the wind was a crucial factor. Battles were won or lost by the shrewd exploitation of shifts in the breeze. The advent of steam changed all that. Then air warfare at sea brought back the constraints. The earliest biplanes took off from tiny decks, without mechanical aids, due to the wind generated over the deck by the forward motion of the ship. As aircraft and their loads became increasingly heavier, mechanical aids like arrester wires and various forms of catapult became standard deck equipment. The wind, however, still plays a vital role in the successful deployment of modern airpower at sea, and at times, it can restrict it severely.

In a task force centered on a large carrier, its battle formation is dictated by the wind direction, because the carrier is obliged to steam into the wind to launch and recover its aircraft. So, in spite of whatever the tactical situation around him may be, the carrier commander steams into the wind, which is most unlikely to be blowing straight down his deck at the time. As the carrier turns away to launch aircraft, other units of the task force must either detach to protect it, or the carrier is left on its own, unprotected by the anti-submarine screen for relatively long periods. Especially in coastal waters, carrier commanders have found that nature, in all its perversity, often forces them to steam towards the hostile shore to get that wind over the deck. When the natural wind is light, there are two other important factors. It means that the carrier has to accelerate to high speed to generate wind over the deck, for mile after mile during launch and recovery. On a big, oil-burning carrier that can mean gulping fuel at one gallon every ten yards, and in low winds, carriers are often obliged to steam at an angle to the swell. This increases the motion of the ship at critical periods and results in a lot of missed approaches and even landing accidents. Although the Sea Harrier does carry more weapons in short takeoff with the wind aiding lift, the airplane *can* take off vertically using its own launch power, independently of wind. Once again, independent of wind, *all* landings are vertical.

As on land, the Harrier at sea is most productive in the STOVL mode—short takeoff and vertical landing. Its minimum takeoff run is zero for vertical takeoff, and that is how it will be used in some situations. For example, scrambling vertically from the deck in rapid reaction to lay a sonobuoy screen, its total time from scramble alarm to drop point thirty miles away is six minutes. Using Sea Harriers for this could relieve anti-submarine helicopters of the need to carry armament and give them a better capability with their detection gear. However, in most situations, there is the inevitable trade-off between takeoff run and weapons load. For every foot of deck run, the Harrier can carry six pounds more fuel or weapons, and for every knot of wind the ship's speed generates over the deck, the payload leaps by sixty-six pounds. That can add up to a lot of extra weapons. As we'll see later, an exciting innovation, the Ski Jump, offers even more dramatic payload benefits.

The Harrier is no different from any other aircraft in its

inability to carry its maximum payload from its minimum takeoff run. Since its minimum takeoff run *is* zero, then the benefits to any Air Group commander are great. The aircraft can start up and lift off, from wherever it is parked on the deck, within two minutes. There is no time-consuming taxiing or marshalling as with conventional aircraft. A group of Harriers can take off simultaneously. They need separation of only thirty feet between aircraft for vertical takeoff, and there is no need for the carrier to change course or speed into wind.

Deck landing accidents have long been related to approach speed. This is a fact of naval aviation life which encouraged the development of arrester gear, angled decks, mirror landing sights and other complex deck aids. The precise point through which the naval pilot must aim on his final approach to the deck is known as the "gate." He must hold a precise speed of up to 130 knots, and keeping a precise heading, he must pass through this "gate" which is seldom greater than fifteen feet wide and thirty feet deep. Imagine what it is like when the deck is pitching and rolling at the same time. It is clearly not a job for the fainthearted or the unskilled, but the adrenalin that conventional fixed wing pilots expend on deck landing, the Harrier pilot can save for combat. In the decelerating transition from wingborne to hovering flight, he does not even have to aim at the ship. Errors of speed can be corrected by adjusting the length of the transition to the hover. In the final hover, if the deck is partially blocked, the Harrier can "air-taxi" to a clear part of the deck. Kinetic energy, the energy associated with motion, has always been the problem in recovering heavy aircraft at sea. The Harrier gets rid of that energy, before it lands, not after it has hit the deck.

Bill Bedford's sortie to the *Ark Royal* in 1963 was the first deck landing by the prototype P1127 aircraft. The first full-fledged Harrier to operate from a carrier deck was a demonstration flight from the Italian vessel, *Andrea Doria*, in October 1967. Then, in March 1970, two R. A. F. Harriers flying off the Royal Navy's H. M. S. *Eagle* cleared the airplane for British service deck operations. However, the pilots who were faced with proving the concept in operational terms were the aviators of the U. S. Marine Corps. After all, they bought this little foreign airplane "off the shelf" for the very purpose of operating off ship decks in support of their amphibious landing troops. No pilots ever had a greater incentive to confound the critics of a new airplane.

Lt. Colonel Bud Iles and Major Marx Branum were the Marine Corps pilots assigned in February 1971, to the initial service trials of the new aircraft on the 18,300 ton helicopter assault ship, U. S. S. *Guadalcanal*, and the amphibious transport dock ship, U. S. S. *Coronado*, at sea off the Naval Air Test Center, Patuxent River. The *Guadalcanal* had a flight deck of 590 feet x 105 feet. The task of the two pilots was to prove the Harrier was really compatible with shipboard operation, and to confirm standard operating procedures. For five days, they flew intensively, making seventy sorties in all. They would do short takeoffs carrying about 4,000 pounds of weapons, drop their ordnance and recover by vertical deck landing. At the end of these initial trials, the report said that the Harrier could be operated satisfactorily both day and night from helicopter assault ships. Marx Branum, on the basis of his one and only night landing on the *Coronado*, had well-justified reservations about night operations from amphibious transport dock ships. These ships have a well deck which can be flooded to allow landing craft to operate from them. Their flight deck is at the other end, aft of the superstructure, a platform about 200 feet x 80 feet.

It was a dark night with no horizon visible, and about twenty knots of wind. Marx Branum went up in a helicopter and had a look. There was a faint glow from Norfolk, Virginia. He decided to give it a try. The deck of the *Coronado* was aft of the superstructure, so to take advantage of landing into the wind Branum did not want it blowing straight down the bow. He wanted it at an angle of about thirty degrees across the deck, but as the wind and the sea state happened to be in the same direction, the ship was forced to turn at thirty degrees to the angle of the waves. The deck was pitching and rolling drunkenly as he did a vertical takeoff and settled into his first approach. He did not decelerate quite fast enough and still had about fifteen knots of forward speed as he came up to the deck. The deck reference lights he was relying upon slipped past under the nose and wings as he came to the hover. On the deck, his colleagues without the benefit of a horizon, could not tell whether the Harrier was climbing or descending or whether the ship was pitching. It was a classic disorientation situation. Marx had his doubts, too. He made the transition back into wingborne flight, went round again, and this time managed to make a fairly respectable vertical landing. They had planned eight landings, but Marx and Bud Iles reckoned they had collected quite enough data from one! It was clear that on a deck that small—about one-third the size of the *Guadalcanal*—routine night operations would require some kind of acceptable center line lights and a glide slope indicator.

In view of the U.S. Navy's recent commitment to V/STOL, the next stage of the Marines' shipboard trials had a far-reaching significance. During this stage, and later, on the the U.S.S. *Franklin D. Roosevelt*, the Marines, in effect, "loaned" themselves to the Navy to allow their "big brother" to study the use of V/STOL in their own air-sea warfare role. On September 23, 1974, six Harriers of VMA 513 departed Norfolk, Virginia, on the U.S.S. *Guam*. The *Guam*, an 18,300 ton helicopter assault ship like the *Guadalcanal*, had been designated the Navy's "interim" sea control ship. The airplane was to perform so impressively from the little flat top, that the seeds were sown then for the Navy's swing to V/STOL.

U. S. Marine Corps Harrier of VMA 542 (Tiger Squadron) lands vertically on the deck of the U. S. S. Guam, *during Exercise Solid Shield, 1974.*

The Harriers' mission was to combine with a helicopter squadron to support the 32nd Marine Amphibious Unit which, when they reached the Mediterranean, would be Task Force 62. They reached the Mediterranean in the second week in October and started to fit into the scheme of amphibious maneuvers established for the Sixth Fleet. The Harrier mission, in the combined exercise which followed, was to provide close air support for the helicopters, suppress ground fire in the landing zones, and once the beachhead was established, to supply close air support by quick reaction vertical takeoff from the deck of the *Guam.* Because of the small number of Harriers involved, heavy air cover was supplied by the aircraft of the carrier U.S.S. *Saratoga*. The Harriers also flew intercept missions against aircraft like the Tupolev 20 Bear, the Russian recce aircraft which were shadowing the fleet.

There were six ships, including the U.S.S. *Guam*, in the Mediterranean Amphibious Ready Group, which comprised the Sixth Fleet's landing force. By this time, although the amphibious transport dock ship still was not cleared for night operations, the *Guam* had been given a rudimentary glide slope indicator to help night landing. It had three prisms. The bottom prism was red for low, the center one was amber for "you're on the correct glide path," and the green one was for high. It was not ideal, but combined with approach information given by radio from the landing control officer on deck, another Harrier pilot, they were able to make controlled approaches to the hover and land vertically at night.

At the end of the six months on the *Guam*, the Harriers of VMA 513 had shown they could fly all the missions necessary to support an amphibious assault. They had shown that their six aircraft could operate away from the support facilities of their parent squadron for a long period of time on a small ship. But, most crucial to the Marines' concept of operation, they had shown that they could fly off such small ships alongside helicopters. Most of the worries had been about the operation of the command structure. The officers on the *Guam* were used to controlling helicopters. Now, fast-moving fixed wing aircraft were introduced into their well-ordered existence. With normal fixed wing aircraft the interface was less of a problem because they were flown and controlled from a separate ship (a large conventional carrier), and the helicopters were flown from their own vessel. The trials on the *Guam* integrated this fast-moving jigsaw.

Typically, the first launch of helicopters loaded with troops, spaced themselves on the deck, launched, and orbited on the port side of the *Guam*. The second launch joined them, and then the Harriers moved forward from their parking places at the rear, did a short takeoff and reported on radio to the Tactical Air Control (TAC) center on the *Guam*. The Harriers orbited at a holding point off the beach, while the helicopter assault force and the amphibious troops were given coordinated landing times: "L" hour for the beach landing and "H" hour for the inland helicopter assault landing.

The Harriers were vectored over by TAC to accompany the helicopters into the beach doing low level, high speed runs to suppress enemy fire, then switching their mission several miles inland to attack any enemy ground forces around the helicopter landing area. Then, they returned to the *Guam* by vertical landing, re-armed and sat there in the cockpit, listening in on FM radio to the same frequency as TAC. The forward air controller who was landed with the helicopter assault troops requested air support and gave the target and map coordinates to TAC. The Harrier pilots simultaneously marked the target and coordinates on their maps. A push of the start button, takeoff vertically, and they were streaking inland again in sections of two. The lessons learned during that intensive six months on the *Guam* have laid the groundwork and become the model for the typical Marines amphibious task force of the future.

It may not make any difference to a Harrier itself whether it is being flown from a ship's deck or from dry land, but it can have an unnerving effect on pilots new to ship deck operations. The visual cues for hovering beside a ship could not be more different from land. Pilots who have never done it before can be almost literally mesmerized as they come to the hover beside this enormous iron machine pounding through the heaving water at thirty knots. All the spray and waves can make a pilot very easily lose his concentration. He may be nicely alongside the ship and apparently in the hover, when, in fact, he could have a fair bit of forward speed still on the airplane. It may sound perfectly self-evident that if you fly alongside a ship you will appear to be hovering even though you clearly must have forward speed to be maintaining that constant position beside it. It can be even more confusing if the ship is steaming at twenty knots into a twenty-five knot wind.

Sitting alongside that ship in the hover, the Harrier will appear not to be moving in respect to the ship, though it will have an actual forward air speed of forty-five knots. In circumstances like that, it is absolutely vital that the pilot keeps his eye on his instruments, and believes what they tell him. For if he does have about forty-five knots of air speed and tries a brisk sideways movement as if he were in a still-air hover, then he could be in serious trouble due to the rolling moments generated by the sideslip. Despite the illusion that he has been sitting in a peaceful hover preparatory to landing vertically, he has, in fact, still been rushing through the air. Once he gets down low over the deck, it may be pitching and rolling and heaving underneath the aircraft and disorientation can be a real problem. The gentle movement of the aircraft, say to the left, may give the pilot the distinct impression that he is moving to the right, because the motion of the deck is much faster than his maneuver. So, the difficulty lies not in the physical handling of the aircraft, but in the mental effort of rejecting confusing visual clues in this new environment.

Vertical takeoff on ships is exactly the same as on land, but short takeoffs are quite different. On a runway when the pilot puts the nozzles down and jumps into the sky, the earth is still roughly at the same level in front of him, and he can judge whether he is still going up and away. On a ship, when he puts the nozzles down at the end of the deck, it is like taking off over a cliff. The visual judgement he had on the flight path, away from a runway on land, just does not exist, so it is much harder to judge climb or dive relative to a moving surface fifty feet below the nose, when the aircraft unsticks. The emphasis here is on very careful checks before takeoff on trim, nozzle angle stops and flaps, because if any of these are set wrong and do not behave exactly as they should on take-off, the character of the short takeoff at sea reduces the chances of noticing the error.

A device which has had almost as much influence on the operation of V/STOL aircraft from ships as the Harrier itself had on shipboard operation, was the Ski Jump take-off ramp. Just like the Harrier, the concept was so simple that one was tempted from the outset to think that there had to be a penalty somewhere. Experience has shown none. And the two other naval Harrier operators are equally convinced of its benefits— Ski Jumps are being fitted to both the Indian Navy's carrier *Vikrant* and to the new Spanish carrier the *Principe de Asturias*. A Ski Jump was built into the design of the new Italian aircraft carrier *Giuseppe Garibaldi*—they're actively considering either Sea Harriers or AV-8Bs.

What happens to a Harrier after a short takeoff along this upward curving ramp could best be compared to a stone thrown upwards. The stone has a longer time of flight than one thrown parallel to the ground. This time of flight from the ramp is used to increase speed on the Harrier, allowing the wings to start working. The speed increase is what an ordinary aircraft achieves running along a runway, but of course because the Harrier is designed to hover, it does not need this speed for control. It can afford to be in the sky during the acceleration if something will give it the initial time of flight necessary. That something else is the Ski Jump.

Its principal effect is a dramatic reduction in the length of short takeoffs with full weapon and fuel loads. It is a classic example of an idea so brilliantly simple that one wonders why no one thought of it before. The man who did first think of it was a Royal Navy engineering officer, Lt. Commander Doug Taylor, and he presented the idea in a thesis written at Southampton University in 1973. He based his paper on the idea of an airplane with sufficient thrust to accelerate initially in an upward trajectory off the Ski Jump, and by the time it had descended in its trajectory to a height around its initial launching point, it would be flying completely on its wings. There was only one aircraft capable of both that acceleration and of being controllable, by its reaction controls, at speeds below the stall during the trajectory. It was the Harrier.

Taylor approached Hawker Siddeley who gave their qualified support, while they examined it thoroughly. Taylor's concept was subjected to the close scrutiny of Hawker's expertise. At the end of their study, they pronounced the principles sound. Their enthusiasm now equalled Taylor's, and from late 1975 when the Ministry of Defense placed study contracts with them for a Ski Jump, they have championed the new idea as an ideal marriage between their aircraft and its operation at sea.

The basic actions of the Harrier pilot using Ski Jump takeoff are the same as in his takeoff from a normal flat deck. He accelerates, with jet nozzles horizontal, into the curved ramp. As the aircraft reaches the top of the ramp, he deflects the nozzles to fifty degrees and enters the upward trajectory. At a twenty degree angle, the Ski Jump cuts takeoff distance by over half. In payload, that could mean as much as 2,000 pounds more than from the same length of flat deck giving the same launch speed.

There are other benefits, not so obvious, but equally important. In peacetime, flying from conventional aircraft carriers ceases when deck pitching exceeds plus or minus around ten feet of vertical motion at bow and stern. Normal fixed wing aircraft, launched from a pitching deck, bow down, require extra launch air speed to curve the flight path away from the sea. However, on an upward trajectory of twenty degrees from the Ski Jump, the Harrier could safely leave the bow at virtually any point in the pitching cycle. Taken to its extreme limits, though, the deck crew might

Ski Jump in operation.

have strong feelings about their own ability to stay out of the sea!

Flight safety is another major benefit. In a normal flat deck short takeoff, the Harrier pilot begins his transition to wingborne flight soon after he leaves the end of the deck, by progressively rotating the nozzles aft. At this stage, he is around flight deck height, about fifty feet above the waves, and there is little margin for error. However, in the Ski Jump trajectory the Harrier pilot commences his transition to conventional wingborne flight hundreds of yards ahead of the ramp exit, and most important, 200 feet higher. In an emergency where nozzles stubbornly remain aft at launch, the flat deck takeoff aircraft will hit the sea in 2.5 seconds. From a Ski Jump launch at the same weight, the time to impact is 6.5 seconds. Consider that the minimum time required for a pilot to react to an emergency and eject is two seconds, and it is clear which of these two options the naval aviator would prefer.

The safety discussion has another intriguing aspect. Normally, the heavier the aircraft is in these takeoff emergency situations, then the more critical things become. This is not true with Ski Jump. The greater the weight, the greater the upward momentum, and the longer the trajectory time. Thus, it is even conceivable that swift jettisoning of weapons from underwing pylons could allow a pilot to eliminate the prob-

lem and save the aircraft by accelerating to wingborne speed, jets aft.

The normal Harrier short takeoff run from a flat deck at maximum weight, takes say 600 feet to the point at the end of the deck where the pilot swivels the nozzles aft and starts the transition to wingborne flight. In the Ski Jump, the point at which the transition commences is at the top of the trajectory or about 1300 feet ahead of the ramp. The Ski Jump runway is therefore over twice as long as that needed for the

Ski Jump.

First Ski Jump Trials, August 1977. John Farley flies a Harrier loaded with three 1,000 lb. bombs off the 6 degree ramp at R.A.E., Bedford within a week of the first lightweight launches.

flat deck STO. In the words of the inventor, Lt. Commander Taylor, "It may be twice as long, but most of that runway is in the sky."

The *Kiev*, the first aircraft carrier built by the Soviet Union, sailed into the Mediterranean in July 1976. She is the first of a new line of vessels which the Russians will deploy throughout the oceans of the world in their increasing global role. However, it was the aircraft on her decks which altered the equation of air power at sea. The Soviet Union had decided from the outset that their air power would land and

Three views of the YAK 36 "Forger" on the Kiev *in 1976, including (bottom right) a side view of the aircraft in heavily auto-stabilized hover above the deck.*

take off vertically. NATO codenamed the *Kiev*'s new fighters "Forger." Since the public demonstration of their experimental vectored thrust aircraft, "Freehand" at Domodedovo in 1967, the Russians had been expected to produce an operational version, but its exact form took most observers by surprise. It has two engines installed forward of the center of gravity purely for lift, and one at the rear with the dual function of lift, via two swivelling nozzles, and cruise, once the Forger has made the transition to wingborne flight.

Forger seems to have been designed purely for vertical takeoff from the deck, so inevitably it has a considerably reduced maximum payload, compared with the Harrier with its short takeoff capability. It appears that the Soviet aircraft is capable of lifting off with a combat load of around 2,200 pounds, depending on atmospheric conditions. This compares with the 8,000 pounds which the Harrier has already flown on short takeoff and which will become the norm for the advanced Marine Corps version, the AV-8B. There are four underwing pylons capable of carrying rocket and gun pods, air to air missiles, bombs, recce pods or extra fuel tanks. The Forger's lack of any hard points for weapons carriage on wings or fuselage, and its folding wings to make space on the hangar deck, would seem to preclude any significant increase in payload capacity on this version.

Two versions of Forger have been identified, the single seat version, codenamed Forger A, and the two seat trainer dubbed Forger B. Both versions are mid-wing monoplanes. The lift-cruise engine at the rear gives 14,500 pounds of thrust and the two lift engines in tandem just behind the cockpit give a combined thrust of 12,500 pounds. The engines are designed to produce a balanced lift around the center of gravity in the VTOL mode. The loss of any one of these engines would almost certainly result in a crash. Experts who have studied intelligence films of Forger flights from the *Kiev* believe the aircraft is controlled in roll in the hover by Harrier-type puffers at the wing tips. It is thought that pitch is controlled by thrust from the differential pipes of the lift engines and can be moved to give yaw control. The landing and takeoff phases have been so steady, that some observers believe there must be a computer-controlled auto-stabilization system.

The *Kiev* itself, and its sister ship the *Minsk*, possess a formidable array of weapons. Western observers believe its primary missions are to hunt and kill Polaris/Poseidon submarines and to launch long range missile attacks against U.S. Navy aircraft carriers. Apart from the fixed wing jets, there are around twenty Kamov Ka-25 helicopters for search and destroy missions against nuclear powered submarines. The *Kiev* is designed to operate as a self-contained unit in hostile areas where there is a high threat from carrier and land-based enemy aircraft. It has gun and missile systems for short and medium range defense against this threat, as well as torpedo launchers and anti-submarine missile and rocket launchers. The primary role of the fifteen or so Forgers on the *Kiev* would seem to be reconnaissance in the local air-space around the carrier and to provide mid-course guidance aids for the SS-N-12 anti-shipping missiles as they race to their targets at almost three times the speed of sound. Forger could also be used to intercept enemy patrol and anti-submarine aircraft like Orion and Nimrod which were just outside the range of the *Kiev*'s defensive missile screen.

However, on the *Kiev*'s voyage from the Black Sea to Murmansk in the summer of 1976, Western intelligence decided that Forger's radius of operation would be hampered by the long, slow transition necessary for changing from the hover and back again. It not only made it vulnerable to attack during this phase, but the one and a half minutes it took for the transition in each direction was estimated to use up about 30 per cent of its internal fuel per sortie. Carrying internal fuel only, plus 2,200 pounds of weapons, it is estimated that Forger has a mission radius of around 130 nautical miles. Operating against maritime patrol aircraft, the Forger with two heat seeking infrared missiles, and two 100 gallon drop tanks would be able to stay "on station" for an hour 100 nautical miles from the *Kiev*. In this air defense role, the Forger's limited radar capability does not compare to the multi-mode Blue Fox fitted to Sea Harrier. In air combat Forger's two swivelling rear nozzles do not allow it to use VIFF like the Harrier.

The Forger, of course, was not designed as a classic attack aircraft. Its role is different. Although it doesn't bear comparison with the world's only other operational VTOL airplane, it is safe to assume the Soviet development effort is not standing still. No doubt the pioneering work of the U.S. Marine Corps with true V/STOL aircraft supporting amphibious landings has been noted by the Soviet strategists thinking ahead to the Forger replacement.

The four navies now operating Harriers are the Royal Navy, the United States Navy through the Marine Corps squadrons, the Spanish Navy, and the Indian Navy. The Spaniards have renamed it the Matador, and they operate six single-seaters and two two-seaters off the pride of their fleet, the wooden deck aircraft carrier, S.N.S. *Dedalo* and they now have 12 AV8B's on order. The Spanish Navy had been operating only helicopters without any fixed wing air power at all, but they were following the progress of the Harrier through its introduction into R.A.F. and Marine Corps service, and particularly its highly successful shipboard trials. In October 1972, they took the plunge and asked Hawker Siddeley to demonstrate the Harrier for them. Deputy chief test pilot John Farley flew from Dunsfold airfield to the carrier, which was in the Mediterranean off Barcelona. Farley's brief was to convince the high-powered group on board, which included twelve admirals, that the Harrier was a high performance jet which had all the flexibility of their helicopter squadrons. He ran the gamut of takeoff modes, put on an aerobatic display, and in high speed runs fired the 30 mm. guns at targets being towed behind the *Dedalo*. The helicopter pilots were very excited about the prospects of getting the Harrier, but the admirals were calm, cool and very businesslike, and they asked searching questions.

There could have been a temptation in discussing a multimillion dollar deal like this, to "oversell" the airplane and tell prospective customers like the Spaniards, that it would require very little training to convert to V/STOL. John Farley's view was that this was simply going to be counterproductive in the long term. Over a cup of coffee, he told a Spanish admiral, "Your pilots have never flown a jet before. They've got to learn how to fly a conventional jet fighter, like any raw pilot, before they can even begin to climb into a

Harrier." There were no further questions and the British team returned to England.

As it turned out, Farley's honesty did nothing to deter the *Armada Espanola*. His flying display had been enough to convince them the Harrier was the airplane they needed. They announced that they were ordering Harriers for their navy, then quietly selected a team of pilots and sent them to America for the regular U.S. Navy fixed wing jet training program. They did about forty hours on the A4 Skyhawk and about the same again converting to Harriers. Though they had never flown high performance jets, they were all experienced airmen with 600–800 hours on helicopters. It is a tribute to their caliber that only two failed fixed wing training, and another dropped out during the Harrier conversion course.

The *Dedalo's* wooden decks were waterproofed with pitch in the gaps between the planks. The jet efflux on Farley's demonstration did a marvellous job in softening and smoothing out this pitch, and the Spaniards thanked him for the use of this sophisticated heating device! It actually improved the waterproofing, but vertical takeoffs from the same spot might have eventually blown the pitch clean away, so the *Dedalo* flight deck has now been covered with a thin metal sheet to protect the pitch, and form a VTOL pad amidships.

The Royal Navy's Sea Harriers operated in the first instance from the 20,000 ton "through-deck" ASW carrier H.M.S. *Invincible*. It was designed for use by a helicopter group, before the Royal Navy was given back their fixed wing air power. *Invincible* and her two planned sister ships, *Illustrious* and *Ark Royal,* are not purpose-built platforms for V/STOL operations. However, her conventional flat deck was transformed by the installation of a ski jump. The planned aircraft complement on each of the *Invincible* class ships was five Harriers plus up to twelve Sea King helicopters.

Sea Harrier over H.M.S. Invincible. *The ship and the aircraft which, from the early 1980's, will change the entire style of fixed-wing jet air power at sea.*

Clearly, though, the advent of Ski Jump is a major influence on any future ships and, in theory, naval air power could be spread throughout a fleet right down to the single Harrier operating from a ship displacing perhaps as little as 4,000 tons. The limiting factor will be where the smallness of the ship produces deck movements so violent that operations would be unpractical in all but the best weather.

Chapter 13

The Super-Harrier: The Harrier II/AV-8B

By the late 1980's the U.S. Marine Corps plans that their entire light attack airpower will be composed entirely of jump jets. These aircraft will be 340 advanced versions of the Harrier—the Harrier II known in America as the AV-8B. This would represent the pinnacle of the pioneering work the Marines have invested right through the thick and thin of a revolutionary aviation concept which has seemed poised for oblivion on several occasions. The Harrier started the revolution in tactical air power, particularly at sea, but it was the Marines who took the little airplane and proved the concept again and again, until the most entrenched critics were forced to sit up and take notice. The AV-8B is the culmination of a brilliant development program which will have doubled the aircraft's performance while scarcely adding to its basic weight or size.

There is a bitter irony in the AV-8B for many of those in Britain who were involved in the Harrier project from the outset. Lack of Defense money in the U.K. has meant that this product of British inventive genius may shift irrevocably over the Atlantic. Britain will continue to receive royalty payments on the Harrier airframe until the License Agreement runs out in 1984, but her role over the next few years will be that of a subcontractor supplying parts of the airframe for the American manufacturers, McDonnell Douglas. Rolls Royce is going to share in the production of the Pegasus for the AV-8B with Pratt and Whitney of America. Yet, if certain plans had reached fruition, then Britain might have been participating as a full partner in the advanced airplane.

In the autumn of 1972, the U.S. Navy put out a letter to the American aircraft industry inviting ideas for the next generation of V/STOL aircraft. The Marines were stunned when the list of candidates for further study was announced. It did not include any development of the Harrier. Taken to its conclusion, and assuming no action by the Marines, this would have resulted in the AV-8A Harrier eventually reaching the end of its useful life with nothing to replace it except a conventional aircraft or some other form of V/STOL which the Navy would by then have decided they should have. It looked as if the Navy were trying to kill off the Harrier program.

The type they were favoring was the North American Rockwell XFV 12 project which is even now bidding as the supersonic Navy V/STOL fighter for the 90's. It has a thrust-augmented wing which bleeds the total exhaust flow of the main power plant and ejects it through a venetian blind arrangement in the wings to give vertical capability. If the U.S.N. were to pursue that course without any further development plans for the Harrier then it was bad news. This was the Navy's first act of hostility towards the Harrier. The news spread despair through Marine aviation headquarters. However, they had not fought so hard for the program in the first place, only to allow it now to degenerate into age and obsolescence. It was time to play politics again.

Colonel Dick Marsh, then managing the Harrier Program in Naval Air Systems Command in Washington, D.C., sat one Saturday morning with some other senior colleagues and devised a program aimed at grabbing the Navy's interest once more in the development of the Harrier. Marsh made a transatlantic telephone call to his English counterpart, Air Commodore Eric Burchmore, and set in motion a train of events which was to result in a high level team from the British Ministry of Defense flying to Washington. Marsh's plan was for an AV-16 using the uprated Pegasus 15 engine with the aim of doubling AV-8A performance. Burchmore had been taking advantage of his first free time for weeks, to wallpaper his bathroom at home with an intricate pattern. He just reached the last sheet of paper when the phone rang. They spoke for about half an hour, and when he ran back upstairs the paper had stuck together in a horrible, unusable tangle. The jigsaw repair he was forced to make in the top corner is still pointed out to visitors as "Marsh's Folly!"

The top civil servant in the Ministry's procurement executive, Air Marshal Sir Peter Fletcher, Controller Aircraft, flew to America with Burchmore for secret talks with the U.S. Navy. There was little doubt from these talks that the Navy had indeed been about to cast aside the "four poster" concept of V/STOL, but this clever piece of maneuvering by the Marine Corps proved decisive, and the groundwork was laid during that visit, for the AV-16. A joint U.S.-U.K. team was formed to study the advanced Harrier. Once again, the Marines were involved in intensive lobbying on the Hill, and they also used the press very effectively. As one officer put it, "We did not discourage articles in the press which supported the Harrier concept of V/STOL." There seemed to be a growing interest in the Marines' new aircraft, and disinterested third parties could be produced at the drop of a hat for statements supporting the Harrier. The Navy couldn't have failed to be aware of what was going on. At Naval Air Systems Command, Navy officers wryly commented, "I see there's been yet another pro-Harrier feature!"

The AV-16 was to involve a redesigned modified airframe, but most important, it was to have a completely new engine, with a bigger fan. The Pegasus 15 would produce around 25,000 pounds thrust. That is 3,000 pounds more than the current Pegasus 11 which powers the AV-8A Harrier. After a year's work by the four companies involved—Hawker Siddeley, McDonnell Douglas, Rolls Royce, and Pratt and Whitney—a thick pile of reports was produced for Naval Air Systems Command. They took a long look, and recoiled. The provisional price which was being attached to the AV-16 development program was 1,000 million dollars, of which around 500 million dollars alone was to develop and "Americanize" the engine. All that money for 3,000 pounds' extra thrust did not seem like cost-effectiveness.

At that time, the U.S. Navy themselves had no requirement for this new V/STOL aircraft. However, in spite of this stumbling block, the AV-16 had come very near to being "sold" in America, when the U.K. government announced that they were pulling out through lack of money. The AV-16 project died right there and then. There was no way for the U.S. government to fund it at such cost for what was to them a relatively small number of aircraft.

This did nothing, though, to change the burning desire of the Marine Corps to have their all-V/STOL light attack force of advanced Harriers in the 1980's. In St. Louis, Missouri, engineer Larry Smith of McDonnell Douglas got together with some colleagues from NASA to work on ways of giving the AV-8A a significant increase in performance without spending vast sums of money on engine and airframe development.

NASA had been working on some mathematical and physical modelling of arrangements of vectored thrust with their nozzles situated under the wing so that they gave a positive circulation of air around the wing, as opposed to the negative circulation which happens on the AV-8A. Using money approved by Congress, which had been left over from the AV-16 program, McAir put an AV-8A model in the NASA wind tunnel and discovered they were losing about 3,000 pounds of lift on short takeoffs on the AV-8A due to this negative lift. When the nozzles were put down for short takeoff, the front nozzles set up a pumping motion and sucked air from the top of the wing downwards, spoiling vitally needed lift just as the aircraft was leaving the ground. They decided to cure that by moving the wing chord forward, changing the angle of sweep and positioning the wing flaps very close to the rear nozzles, thus getting positive pumping action from those nozzles and, at the same time, reducing the negative action from the front nozzles. It was engineering in the highest tradition of the aircraft — simple and brilliant. This new arrangement of wing flap and nozzle configuration was now giving what they described as a positive circulation flow over the wing in STO, and it promised 6,000 pounds more lift than the AV-8A. Now, from a development point of view that sort of performance improvement at very low cost was staggering. They still had not finished.

It was known that in vertical takeoff, the engine was starving itself of air because of the inlet design which was basically the same as that for the Pegasus 6 engine back in the Harrier Mk 1 days. They scaled the inlet, jointly designed by HSA and McAir for the Pegasus 15 in AV-16, to a size suitable for the Pegasus 103. This intake has two rows of auxiliary doors and a better lip profile. That redesign alone gave them 600 pounds of extra thrust from the same engine as the AV-8A.

On the gun pods under the fuselage, HSA had successfully experimented, in 1959–1960, with devices which would give additional lift by breaking up the suction created under the airplane during vertical takeoff. McDonnell took it fur-

ther. They put longer strakes and a little dam at the forward
end of the two gun pods which actually captured the energy
reflecting upwards from the jet exhaust and gave an extra upward boost which helped overcome the suck-down effect.
That was measured at 1200 pounds of extra lift. In the end,
without major redesign of the airframe, except for the intake,
they squeezed an 1800 pounds improvement out of the aircraft in the VTO mode. That was an extra 1800 pounds of
fuel or weapons for combat.

They also redesigned the wing, using what they called a
supercritical aerofoil. This was a thicker wing which increased
internal fuel capacity by 40 per cent better.

The Marine Corps put this whole package together and
presented it as the AV-8 Plus, now known as the AV-8B. Not
surprisingly, Naval Air Systems Command got very excited by
it. Compared to the cost of the modern day development of
an aircraft from scratch, the proposal was very attractive indeed. Large sections of the fuselage and tail were going to be
the same as the AV-8A, and they were using an existing
engine.

Even so, the Harrier concept still had its skeptics and its
enemies. The performance predictions for the AV-8B were
never a stumbling block. There was a solid, proven performance base line with the AV-8A. The issue was still the very
concept of V/STOL close air support itself. The Marines had
shown, in the field, the advantages of reaction time and the
efficiency of "cab rank on the ground" operations, as opposed to the hideously wasteful "cab rank in the sky" of conventional aircraft. As far as they were concerned, the savings
in wartime logistics of aircraft wear and tear, fuel and pilot
fatigue were quite simply overwhelming. People just would
not believe it. This was particularly true of the program analysis branch of the Office of Secretary of Defense, who were
the people responsible for cost-effectiveness.

The Marines won that round with a brilliant analysis by

a McAir engineer, Bob Showers. His analysis showed conclusively that the only thing better than V/STOL close support in terms of reaction time was someone orbiting overhead, and that was prohibitively expensive. The analysis included charts showing reaction times and target decay rates, or the time within which ground troops must get air power if it is to be effective. It was such a fine study that it could not be attacked mathematically or analytically. What finally clinched it was charts analyzing the AV-8B compared to conventional aircraft. It made some other aircraft programs, also vying for money, look so bad in comparison that the AV-8B had no further trouble from an analytical point of view. In fact, when the Marines took some of these charts to Congress, some politicians became very disturbed by the implications. By March 1976, the battle was won and the Secretary of Defense approved the program.

The program has, now run into some difficulties particularly with engine development but it did get off to a very encouraging start when NASA at Ames in California put an AV-8A modified by McAir into the AV-8B configuration in their full-scale wind tunnel. They tried it with different combinations of stores on the pylons and ran the engine to test the new wing flap combination. The performance came out slightly better than McAir had predicted. When they mounted the aircraft on the static test facility at Ames, the new engine inlet combination actually gave a couple of hundred pounds better performance as well.

The first of its type, the wing is non-metal, made of graphite epoxy composite materials, except for the weapon pylons' hard points underneath. This material not only saves a lot of weight on this bigger wing, it is also less likely to corrode in the varying conditions in which the Harrier is operated. What it means in terms of weight is that they get this larger wing area which gives, among other benefits, better maneuvrability, for the same weight as the

Advanced Harrier on test rig at NASA Ames.

AV-8A wing. Instead of two ordnance stations under each wing, it has three, and another under the center line of the fuselage. Instead of two wet stations, where you can put extra fuel tanks, there are four. The outrigger wheels on the wings are now mounted mid-wing for maneuvring on ship decks.

The new aircraft can carry a wide variety of ordnance, including conventional general purpose bombs, cluster munitions. laser-guided weapons, air-to-ground guided missiles like the Maverick and self-defence missiles like the Sidewinder. In a pod under the fuselage it can mount a 25 mm. high velocity, high rate of fire cannon with 300 rounds of ammunition. On its seven store stations, the Harrier II/AV-8B/GR5 can carry either: 16 Mk 82 bombs; 6 BL-755 cluster bombs; 4 300-US gallon external fuel tanks; six Mk 83 bombs; four Maverick air-to-surface missiles; four AIM-9 Sidewinder air-to-air missiles or ten rocket pods. The maximum external load is 9,200 pounds.

British Aerospace sent their own team of engineers to St. Louis to help McAir convert two AV8As into YAV-8Bs—the "Y" representing prototype. This meant grafting on the new engine inlet and, of course, the new "supercritical" wing, on to the AV-8A airframe. It went very smoothly, and the American-British collaborators then got down to the fundamental task of ensuring the aeroplane "came in" under the weight which was being quoted to the customer. Twelve thousand four hundred pounds was the goal. The whole idea of the AV-8B remember, was to double the radius of action/bomb load without any engine development. Even with the clever lift-improvement devices it meant a fairly ruthless attitude towards weight. The ram air turbine system was thrown off the airplane—a modification which has now been carried out on the AV-8A fleet too. The YAV-8Bs finally weighed in 180 pounds under the target.

The first "press-up" (Vertical Take-off) of the YAV-8B took place on November 9, 1978, at the St. Louis headquarters of McDonnell Douglas. A British engineer who was there that day recalled: "There were a lot of white knuckles amongst the Americans. They were worried about the performance of their new wing. I can't think why—all the aircraft needed to support it in the hover, was a bit of wood." It was, perhaps, a revealing remark—Harrier wing design was a sensitive subject.

British Aerospace were, at that time, attempting to convince their own government that the replacement for the R.A.F.'s Harrier GR3s should be their design for a "Big Wing" Harrier. It was to be an uprated Harrier, using the same Pegasus engine, with a larger all-metal wing which was "retrofittable" to the existing Harrier fleet. In 1980, the British government finally rejected this proposal and opted to join the American program with an order for 60 Harrier IIs, to be known as the GR5. There was, however, a strong residual feeling in some parts of British Aerospace—"we build the best sub-sonic fighter wings in the world"—that their rejected wing design would have been better in performance and flying qualities than the aircraft they are now co-operating on.

The AV-8B is heavier, has a bigger wing and a raised canopy. It was never going to be as fast as the original Harrier. But, senior Marine Corps officers will admit that they were "over-optimistic" about the ratio of drag to engine thrust. The drag appeared to be 15–20 per cent higher than expected. McAir thought it was some mysterious drag interference problem they could cure by design. They tried various "fixes" like extended heat shields along the back part of the aeroplane—they feared it might be coming from the engine thrust. None of their efforts had any effect.

So, they went back to square one, right back to the old wind tunnel data of 1971 on the AV-8A. A Naval Air Systems Command engineer, Gene Rooney, did some brilliant scientific detective work and discovered serious errors in the prediction process. Expectations had been raised too high, by the data of almost ten years before.

What it means is that, depending on the weapon load, the AV-8B's maximum speed is around 30 knots slower than the speed predicted—580 knots (.88 Mach) at maximum power at sea level. The problem for the Royal Air Force is that their version is going to be heavier, because of extra equipment, including electronic counter measures gear, for the European theatre. So, an improvement in maximum speed is of considerable importance to them.

The manufacturers have redesigned the engine inlet, and this gives some more thrust. They are also considering reshaping the lower surface of the wing, and modifying the shape of the AV-8B's raised canopy compared with the Sea Harrier's. In a number of respects, the performance of the full scale development models—the first flew in November 1981— is less than the YAV-8B prototype, so they're analyzing the differences between the two aircraft, the hybrid YAV-8B and its "half-brother" the AV-8A. They've also partly compensated for the increased drag by increasing the length of time a pilot can use his combat rating—that's opening the throttle beyond the normal maximum setting and using a bit more r.p.m. and jet pipe temperature on the Pegasus engine. A pilot in combat is not going to worry too much about engine life, but the fact is that using the combat rating not only reduces that life, it also gobbles fuel on this normally highly fuel-efficient engine. However, the Marine Corps have no doubts that it will comfortably fulfil their combat radius requirements. Colonel Jim Orr, the Marines' ex-Harrier program manager said: "This aeroplane has so much range built into it, that any effect on radius of action just doesn't come into our equations. Now, if you were to ask us to hit downtown Moscow—well we might have a problem there!"

John Farley, the British Aerospace Harrier chief test pilot, arrived at Wightman Air Force Base west of St. Louis in November 1979. With him were the other members of a British evaluation team—the CO of "A" fighter test squadron from the government aircraft armament test establishment at Boscombe Down and a R.A.F. Harrier pilot from the operational conversion unit at Wittering. The debate was continuing in England, over whether the R.A.F. should go for the retro-fittable "big wing" Harrier. The brief for Farley and his colleagues was to evaluate the YAV-8B and report whether they believed the aeroplane would perform as McAir said it would. The pilot from Boscombe Down would test the handling of the wing, the Wittering pilot would evaluate low level high speed performance and tactical maneuvring, and Farley himself would look at the V-STOL characteristics. The trip did not get off to a promising start.

The plan was that the Brits would fly ship two—the second of the two prototypes, which incorporated various improvements. American test pilot Jackie Jackson was ferrying the airplane from St. Louis to Wightman when the engine "surged," failed to re-light, and the pilot was forced to

U.S. Marine Corps AV-8B in hover.

U.S. Marine Corps AV-8B, nozzles pointing downwards, for a vertical landing.

U.S. Marine Corps AV-8B makes its first deck landing during sea trials.

eject. Ship two was totally destroyed. McAir were not keen that the British team fly ship one. It took 48 hours of talking to convince them that they should be allowed to fly it a few times, then have it brought up to the standard of the other for a proper evaluation.

John Farley had been told to expect improvements in the V/STOL characteristics of the aeroplane. But nothing had prepared him for the differences, particularly in the short take off and landing phases. "I found the improvements quite staggering, I was tremendously impressed. I felt after those first few flights, that if there were no other changes to the aeroplane, it was a very good value jet indeed."

AV-8B of U.S. Marine Corps Squadron VMAT 203, fore-ground, with AV-8A of the same squadron hovering above.

The design changes which had created these handling benefits were: the enormous flaps, drooped ailerons, and changes to the wingtip reaction control valves which moved them out two-and-a-half feet on each side, and inclined them backwards. Plus of course, the basic aerodynamic changes to the wing.

The flaps almost touch the ground, when extended. The pilot has no direct control over them. Separate actuators are signalled by a computer which tells them when to go down, in relation to the position of the nozzles. The consequences of failure of the flaps to travel down or back again would be severe. If neither goes down you'll either hit an obstacle or go into the sea. If only one goes down the rolling movement generated would be unbelievable, and you'd lose the aircraft immediately. And, if they failed to go back in again, they'd be blown off by the jets. In other words, a pilot must keep his eyes on the two flap indicators. But the extra lift generated was really impressive.

On his first flight in the YAV-8B, John Farley found that he had completely to readjust his thinking to entirely new sets of figures. On short take-off, where he had been accustomed to speeds of 120–130 knots at unstick, he was dealing with speeds like 65 or 70 knots. Instead of approach speeds of 105–110 knots, he was talking of numbers like 60 or even as low as 55 knots. It was a breathtaking difference in the distance required to take off and land. But it wasn't just the performance—it was the beautiful handling that went with it.

In the ordinary Harrier, when the nozzles are put down and the aircraft leaves the ground, there's a very pronounced longitudinal trim change. It comes and goes as the jets initially bounce off the ground and hit the tail of the aeroplane. The result is that the pilot gets completely different airflow over the tail. This means mastering a little trick where the stick is "cycled" some way back initially and then forward and then back to the middle again on every short take-off. In the "B", Farley found he could do a short take-off without moving the stick. What a transformation. And on the approach, the aeroplane was much steadier in all three axes and easier to trim. He found he could even take his hands off and it would stay exactly where it was.

The old aeroplane, although perfectly controllable, was a "touchy little thing" which had to be treated delicately. The "B" had this steadiness in the sky which was truly remarkable. It bore out the old flying axiom "the better the approach, the better the landing." It was rock steady all the way down to the ground, and Farley found he could place it exactly where he wanted to.

There have been accidents throughout the Harrier's existence, in the accelerating and decelerating transitions to and from the hover. In the old airplane, if it started going sideways and one wing developed more lift than the other, the pilot's ability to control this assymetric lift through the reaction control valves was limited. There was only a certain amount of puff, and when that puff was exceeded, the aircraft could roll uncontrollably. The improvement in this area, in the "B", was another revelation.

McAir had responded to some pleading by Ray Searle of British Aerospace, and introduced a very neat and clever bit of engineering to the wingtip roll reaction control valves, by inclining them backwards. If the pilot sits in the ordinary Harrier in a hover and moves the stick over to the right, he's trying to tilt the aircraft to the right, and therefore wants to move to the right. In the ordinary Harrier, if you move the stick to the right in the hover, you blow down with the reaction control valve under the left hand wing to tilt it up, and blow upwards on the right wing to tilt it down. But, because the leading edge of the wing is slightly high in the hover, the valve blowing down is also blowing slightly forwards—thus blowing that wingtip slightly back. The reverse happens on the other wing. The result is that when you bank it to the right, the nose actually goes to the left. The pilot is forced to get in on the act with his rudder to make the aeroplane go the way he wants. The tilting backwards of the reaction control valves had gone a long way towards improving handling in the hover. But just as important, was the great reduction in dihedral effect. John Farley recalled a compelling example. He flew at 120 knots with full rudder on in the middle of a transition, making the YAV-8B go as far sideways as it would go. At the same time he hauled the nose up putting on around 15 degrees of angle of attack—the maximum permitted. The stick remained so close to the centre position, that he actually had to let it go to check if he was using any aileron. The aircraft was so tolerant of going sideways, that he was unable to tell if he needed any roll control power to stabilize it.

There is also an autopilot on board which allows the pilot to fly hands-off in many situations. One can even turn it on for the crucial transition stage of flight. All the pilot then has to worry about is the throttle. Settle in the hover, pull the nose up, ease the throttle lever back, and land.

The British team's test flying lasted for several weeks. They returned to England and presented a broadly favourable first impression.

The advanced Harrier has encountered three significant development problems so far: the thrust/drag ratio discussed earlier; engine "surging" at altitude; and "departures" at high angle of attack.

The first full-scale development AV-8B came along in November 1981. Charlie Plummer, the McDonnell Douglas Harrier project pilot took off on his first sortie to 45,000 feet. He felt a slight thump on the climb-out which he took to be a self-clearing "surge." The Pegasus was still running normally, but he decided to come home. On the ground they laughed and said it couldn't possibly be a surge—it didn't even show on the flight instrumentation. But succeeding flights hit the same barrier at around 35,000 feet. It was decided to abandon that part of the programme and modify an aircraft for engine testing.

John Farley joined the full flight test programme in America in April 1982. By that time the full fleet of four full-scale development aircraft was flying, but ships one, three and four had to be restricted to low or medium altitude to avoid engine difficulties.

Engine surges can be an alarming experience for the pilot. It can be a sound like a hand grenade going off behind the shoulder blades. It's as if the whole airplane has been hit by an enormous hammer blow, and the pilot can immediately fear for the whole structural integrity of his aircraft.

An airplane has an "envelope" within which it can fly without the wing losing flying speed and stalling. If the pilot gets too slow, or has too much angle of attack on his wing, then the wing will stall and the airflow will break down and the lift will vanish. There will be a wing drop, or if the aeroplane is old-fashioned it may even go into a spin. If you rush very quickly towards that stall boundary, and penetrate deeply into the stall circumstances, the end result can be quite violent. You can also, if you know exactly where it is, nibble up to it and actually give, say an underconfident student, a demonstration of the consequences. It's the same with an engine surge.

Inside a turbofan like the Pegasus there are hundreds of little blades on the engine compressors. They are, in effect, like tiny little wings, generating low and high pressure just as aeroplane wings do. There is, however, an aerodynamic limit on these rotating blades. If one of these "wings" stalls it's called a "surge" because that stage of the compressor fails to do its job. The higher pressure that is now behind it, finds it can now move its way forward and it then tends to stall the whole of the compressor, because the pressure distribution has gone wrong. The huge pressure in the engine combustion chamber can now escape out of the front, because it hasn't been beaten by the compressor and forced out of the jet pipe. The more rapidly you approach this point, with lots of power on, the more violent the surge will be.

John Farley's role was to carry out an investigation of the engine surge problem. The method was to set the aircraft up at the speed and height required. With the engine at the test rpm, the aircraft was maneuvred to a pre-briefed point in the flight envelope until there was a thump. The engine was checked, shut down and re-lit if necessary, and another point was tackled with a change in circumstances—altitude, speed, angle of attack, sideslip—until there was another surge. At other times the engine was treated fairly severely, slamming the throttle open and closed.

After a couple of months of this, they had satisfied themselves that the fault did not lie with the airflow being disturbed by the engine intake, the nose or the raised cockpit canopy. It was all very worrying, particularly as the Pegasus had such a remarkable reputation for reliability. And the problem was not restricted to the Harrier II — the Sea Harrier of the Royal Navy was experiencing the same surges. What the two aircraft had in common was a "new build" standard of the Pegasus which, though it was very similar to its predecessors, just wasn't working properly.

The crunch came when they took a really clapped-out old AV-8A engine from the stores at the Pax River test center. They put it in the "B"—and it performed brilliantly. With this engine installed, the new airplane far exceeded the performance it had been giving before. At the time of writing, Rolls Royce engineers are working hard on this problem and have isolated it to the high pressure compressor. The mechanical differences between the two engines are very small—not put in to change it in terms of thrust or fuel consumption, but to make it less corrosion prone, easier to maintain and cheaper to build. The engine problems are not a major concern to the U.S.M.C. or the R.A.F. in their chosen low-level mission, but for the Royal Navy Sea Harrier interceptors and for any possible U.S. Navy use, it would be a very serious matter, were it not solved.

As the test pilots expanded the engine envelope, they were also, inevitably, expanding the airframe envelope. And at high angles of attack and high mach numbers, the airplane was stalling and "departing viciously"—rolling out of control. In the original Harrier there's usually lots of warning if the aircraft is going to depart. "It's like the old Hawker Hunter, it will always tell you what it's doing," said one experienced R.A.F. Harrier pilot. "If you're throwing the airplane around near its limits, it will start to grumble at you. Hold it in that grumble and it'll keep on grumbling. And if you work it too much harder, then it may think of flicking on you. But you can always fly the old Harrier by the seat of your pants without worrying too much about angle of attack limits." Not so with the "B", at this stage. It has British Aerospace-designed extensions at the leading edge of the wings roots, known as LERX, and they, combined with the bigger wing area, have given the new aircraft dramatically increased turning capabilities—even without the use of vectoring in flight. Put an old Harrier up against a "B" in a dogfight, and the new airplane will complete two circles to the old one's single turn through 360 degrees. But LERX, which generate lift at high angles of attack, also suppress the traditional buffeting warnings of stall which the old aircraft had. The departures have occurred at angles of attack beyond what is needed for maximum instantaneous turn rate in combat. But in a dogfight, a combat pilot wants to be able to rack his aircraft round into a turn beyond maximum instantaneous turn rate, so that he can point at another airplane and shoot a missile. The likely answer to this problem is an artificial stall warning, a tone in the cockpit which will tell the pilot when he has reached the optimum angle of attack—the angle beyond which he's going to lose control of the aircraft.

Harry Blot, one of the U.S.M.C. veteran Harrier pilots, and one of their top air combat fliers, is now the Marine Corps' program manager on the Harrier project at Naval Air Systems Command in Washington. He concedes there are some difficulties to iron out, but he considers the Harrier II is a magnificent airplane with all the ingredients to do everything they specified it should do. And he's particularly confident that it will slash the time needed to train new pilots. "It takes us two years to train a pilot now on the AV-8A. On the new airplane we'll have him up and away in a short time. The V/STOL aspect of this airplane is now almost a non-event. It is so much easier an airplane to fly. What's going to limit this airplane is pilot skill—not the limitations of the airframe.

"People talk about the very limited warning of departure in this airplane, compared to the AV-8A. What they forget is that the departures are occurring in an area of the flight envelope where the 'A' couldn't even get to. We haven't even started trying to hack the departure problem. We will. But even if we made zero improvements, our air-to-air envelope is so much bigger than before. There's no way to go but up."

index

A4 Skyhawk 40, 152, 156,
    170, 176, 193, 194, 259
Accidents 30, 31, 114
AFVG 174
Air Data Computer 33–34
Aircraft carriers 233, 234,
    240–2, 243, 250, 254,
    256, 259
Airfield denial 183
Airpower denial 183
Allison Division 167
Amphibious assault 185, 187,
    196
Amphibious operation 190
AMRAAM (advanced medium
    range air-to-air missile)
    237
Andrea Doria 244
Antenna Valley 193, 194
Arctic trials 139
Argosy 87
Ark Royal 107, 108, 233, 243,
    259

Armstrong, Neil 219
Armstrong Whitworth 681,
    110
A10 171, 173
Atlantic Conveyor 59, 237
Attinello, John 208, 209, 211,
    218
Auld, Lieutenant-Commander
    Andy 47
Autostabilization 69, 77, 82,
    135–6
AV-8 Plus see AV-8B
AV-8A (Harrier) 169, 203,
    205, 263, 265
AV-8B (Harrier) 40, 132, 169,
    173, 250, 256, 258,
    261–81
AV-16 263–5
AX 171, 173

Baker, Colonel Bud 152, 155,
    211

283

Balzac   103, 104, 113
Barkhorn, Colonel Gerhard
     117, 119, 120, 122, 126
Barkhorn Turn   119
Barton, Flight Lieutenant Paul
     43
Baseline system   192
Beck, General A. J.   210
Bedford, Bill   233, 243
   crashes aircraft   95–96,
     113–14
   design consultant on P1127
     67–69, 72, 73, 75, 105,
     121
   first carrier landing by
     107–8, 233, 243
   first conventional flight by
     13, 88
   first flight by   76–84
   first free hover by   84–85
   first Harrier XV276 flown by
     145–6
   taxi-ing trials by   86
   test turns by   92–93, 132
   tripartite squadron and
     121, 123, 140
BE53 see Pegasus
Bell X14   73–74
'Big Tee' exercise   191
'Big Wing' Harrier   269, 271
Birdstrikes   31, 140, 232
Blandford, Russ 160, 175
Blot, Major Harry   207, 215,
     280
Blue Falcon   236, 237
Blue Fox   235, 236
Braking stop   27
Branum, Major Marx   244, 245
Bristol Aero Engine Company
     9–10, 17, 100, 108
British Aerospace   269
Broadsword   47
Broadwater, Lieutenant
     Commander Mike   45
BS-100   103

Buccaneer   109
Burchmore, Air Commodore
     Eric   169, 170, 218, 219,
     263

Cab rank missions   188
Cambridge University   17
Camm, Sir Sydney   6, 10, 12,
     14–16, 19, 66, 75, 78, 79,
     85, 126–7
Camouflage   196–7
Campbell, Lieutenant Colonel
     J. K.   117, 120, 210–11
Canberra   45
Center of gravity   23
Centre of thrust   23
CH-53 helicopter   190
CH-53D helicopter   190
Chapman, General Willis
     9–10, 17, 18, 156, 157,
     175
Cheyenne helicopter   171, 173
Chinook   237
Compressor/turbine systems
     23
Computer   138
Connolly, Vice Admiral Tom
     154, 166, 168
Controls   27, 69–70, 75, 105,
     106
Coronado   244
Critical engine speeds   231
Cruise missiles   205
Culpepper, Dick   212, 217, 219
Curtis, Lieutenant Alan   45

Daily Mail Transatlantic Air
     Race   161, 162
Dale, John   23, 96, 127, 229
Dassault, General
     Aeronautique Marcel
     103
Decelerating transition   27, 28

Dedalo 258, 259
Delta Dagger 178
Development problems
    129–47
DME (Distance Measuring
    Equipment) 33
Drag/trust ratio 270

Eagle 244
Edmonston, Flight-Lieutenant
    David 120
Electrical systems 135

F5 fighter 46
F14 Tomcat 208
F15 Eagle 46
F104 Starfighter 128
F115T 5
Fairey FD2 5
Falklands campaign 35,
    43–63, 235, 237
Farley, John 53, 94, 134–44,
    154–5, 162, 163, 254,
    258, 259, 271–8
Farnborough Air Show 147,
    152, 154, 174
Fearless 51
Ferranti Fe 541 32
Fiat G91 light fighter 9
Fixed depression sight 39
Fixed throttle landing
    technique 143
Fleet Air Arm 53, 55, 235
Fletcher, Air Marshal Sir Peter
    263
Flight-refuelling probe 139
Flight-refuelling tests 162
Flying Bedstead 77
Fokkers 101
Forger 235, 255, 256, 257
Forward Air Controller 191
Fozard, John 11, 91, 110, 112,
    145, 146, 161, 215, 218,
    229

Franklin D. Roosevelt 245
Freehand 255
Fuel system 31, 141–4

Gas turbine starter 23
General Motors 167
Giuseppe Garibaldi 250
Graphite epoxy composite
    materials 267
GRMk3 237
Ground loiter 189, 196
Guadalcanal 244
Guam 187, 208, 245–8
Gun pods 265, 266
Gunning, Lieutenant-
    Commander Jock 55
Gutersloh Air Base 195
GVTOL 143, 144
Gyroptere 9
Gyroscopic effect 23, 228

Hall, Sir Arnold 112
Harper, Colonel Ed 169
Harrier Carriers 188, 237
Harris, Flight Lieutenant Pete
    'Bomber' 200–1
Hawk missile 203
Hawker Aircraft Limited 5, 7
Hawker Siddeley 112, 209,
    212, 251, 264
Healey, Denis 110, 146
Helicopter assault ship 244,
    245
Helicopters 233, 235, 238, 247
    259
Henderson, Squadron Leader J.
    122
Hermes 45, 55, 56, 60
High-G Barrel Roll 224
Hiller 2E helicopter 76
Holmes, Lieutenant Bob 45
Hooker, Sir Stanley 9–10,
    17–19, 75, 78, 101, 229,
    230

Hooper, Ralph   8, 11, 15, 70–72, 79, 91, 97, 218
HSA   265
HUD   35, 58, 202
Hunter   5, 7, 14, 15, 33, 58, 66, 279

Iles, Lieutenant Colonel Bud   244
Illustrious   259
INAS   32–38, 41, 192, 202
Indian Navy   258
Indo-Pakistan war   181
Inertial navigation   137
Initial point (IP)   199–200
Intake momentum drag yaw   105, 132
Intrepid   51
Invincible   45, 55, 259, 260
Israel   172
Iveson, Squadron-Leader Bob   60–62

Jackson, Jackie   271
Jet reaction control system   24–26
Johnson, Major A1   120

Kamov Ka-25 helicopter   256
Kennedy, President   115
Kestrel   112, 113, 116–29, 151, 152, 211, 212, 214, 218, 228
Kiev   254, 256, 257

Lary, Lieutenant Colonel Jim   192, 193, 194
La Salle   163
Lasers   38
Leading edge root extensions (LERX)   236, 280

Levy, Larry   115
License agreement   175, 176, 262
Lickley, Bob   114
Lightning   146, 209
Lindell, Colonel Cliff   170
Ling, Lieutenant-Commander Peter   54

McAir   265, 276
McAtee, Captain Willie   55
McCutcheon, Major General Keith B.   152, 160, 165, 167, 169, 177
McDonnell Douglas   158, 159, 176, 262, 264, 269
McDonnell, James S.   161
McGregor, Air Marshal   92–93
McNickle, Lieutenant General Marvin L.   173
Marsh, Bob   112
Marsh, Colonel Dick   263
Matador   258
Maverick   268
Medium Girder Bridge   237, 238
Merewether, Hugh   67, 73–75, 91, 94, 130–1, 230
Metal fatigue   231
MIL 24 Hind troop-carrying helicopter gunships   199
Miller, Colonel Tom   152–4, 156, 157, 159, 164, 177, 211
Minshall, Congressman   173
Minsk   256
Mirage   13, 43, 44, 47, 50, 53, 54, 58, 103, 104, 113
Morgan, Flight-Lieutenant Dave   50
Multi-engine concept   103
Multi-lift engine   102, 109
Munro, Flight-Lieutenant 'Porky'   120

Mutual Weapons Development
Program 9–10, 18, 19,
65, 115

NASA 70–73, 75, 106, 209,
211, 217–19, 264, 265,
267
NATO 9, 101, 102, 104, 183,
195, 198
Navigation display component
36
Navigational systems 33–37
Nene engine 77
New, Colonel Noah 218
Newton, Sir Isaac 24, 25
Nozzle selector lever 24–26
Nuclear warheads 183

Olympus 10
Operational Battlecry 220,
221
Operational requirements 6,
99, 101, 146
Ordnance 268
Orpheus engine 9–11
Orr, Colonel Jim 271

P1103 5, 6
P1121 6–8, 12, 13, 68
P1127 (Harrier)
accident record 30–32
airframe required for
66–67, 81, 89–90
Bell X14 and 73–75
Congressional hearings on
159–60, 164–7, 173, 175,
267
control system 68–69,
72–73, 75, 82–84, 87, 89,
93–94
as fighter
amphibious assault by
185–91

close support missions by
191–5
combat mission, simulated
199–202
deployment in European
war 195–9, 202
low-level flying 202–4
use of, without runways
181–4, 188–9
flight tests on
arctic 139–40
first carrier landing
107–8, 233, 243–4
first conventional 13,
87–89, 90
first free hover 84–85
first tethered flight
74–75, 78–84
re-sideslip 92–94, 132–7
re sortie rate 172
re spinning 129–32
taxi-ing trials 85–87
thrust vectoring 211–13,
215
transitional 90–92
tropical 139–40
free-flight model 71–72
fuel system failures 140–5
future versions of see AV-8B
McDonnell Douglas and 158
159, 176, 262, 264, 265
manufacture of, in America,
proposed 175–6, 261–2
Marine Corps evaluates
151–6
Marine Corps procures
168–76
Marine Corps requests 149,
157–68, 173
NASA and 70–73, 208, 209,
213, 217–20, 264–8
nav/attack system in 32–33,
35, 137–9, 192
Marine Corps 40–41
operational requirement for
99, 101, 102

Phantom compared to   30,
  215, 220–1
Rolls Royce Engine Co.
  opposes   100–2
Ryan Aircraft Corp. supports
  156
SC1 compared to
  76–78, 100–1, 103
thrust vectoring ability of
  advantages of   213–16,
  220–5
  Attinello report on
  208–11
  defined   207–8
  flight tests on   211–13,
  215
  NASA and   217–20
tripartite squadron   105,
  115–28
  design changes   119–21,
  125–6
  information gained from
  123–4, 126, 127
use of, at sea   110
  capabilities relevant to
  235
  carriers for   187–8, 233–4
  design changes to facilitate
  235
  vs. Forger   235, 255–8
  landing and take-off
  problems   247–50
  shipboard trials   243–8
  Ski Jump   242, 250–4
  Spanish Navy   258–9
  V/STOL movements
  24–30
P1150   103
P1154   99–116, 124, 137, 234
Packard, David   171, 172
Pedal shaker   135, 136
Pegasus (BE53) engine   97,
  125, 133, 135
  airframe required by   66–67,
  81, 89–90

financing of   17–19, 65
lightweight front nozzles
  cause of crash   95–96
manufacture in America,
  proposed   262
modifications on
  for combat   216–17
  to increase thrust   101–2,
  137, 152
  to solve problems   227–32
  origins of   10
  principle of   21–23
  thrust vectoring   207–25
Person, Lee   212–14, 217, 219
Phantom   13, 52, 109–11, 146,
  159, 207, 209, 210, 220,
  221
Pitts, Brigadier General
  William   173
Plummer, Charlie   277
Pook, Squadron-Leader Jerry
  62
Poole, Lieutenant-Commander
  David   54
Power failures   140
Pratt and Whitney   166, 262,
  264
Principe de Asturias   250
Project Red Baron   210
Proudfoot, Squadron Leader
  'Hoof'   178
Puffers   68, 69, 77, 82, 212

Radar   58, 235–7
Ramsey, David   54, 55
RB-108 engine   76
RB-162 engine   103
Reconnaissance   40
Reeder, Jack   105, 106, 122
Republic Aviation Company
  101
Rivers, Mendel   160, 170, 175
Rocket pods   138
Rockets   139, 198

Roll-stabilization 40
Rolling vertical landings 140
Rolls Royce 9, 21, 100, 108,
    117, 166, 216, 217, 262,
    264
Rooney, Gene 270
Rosburgh, Major Chuck
    132–4, 137
Royal Air Force 31, 32, 34, 36,
    38, 52, 60, 99, 104–6, 112,
    124, 146, 174, 191, 195,
    198, 202, 209, 225, 270
Royal Navy 106, 234, 258
Ruffle-Smith, Group Captain
    Pat 80
Russell, Colonel Eugene 196
Ryan Aircraft Corporation
    158

Safety record 31, 32
Salt, Lieutenant Colonel 120
SAM missile systems 199, 202
    223
Sanders, Frank 171
Sandys, Duncan 6
Saratoga 247
SATS (Short Airfield Tactical
    Support) 185
Scott, Taylor 53, 55, 59
Scrimgeour, Wing Commander
    David McL. 116, 120, 122,
    124
Sea Eagle 236
Sea Harrier 43–60, 110,
    233–60, 279
Sea Hawk 11
Sea King helicopter 62, 238,
    259
Searle, Ray 276
Seaspray 235
Self-starter 23, 137, 163–4
Shipborne Containerized Air
    Defence System (SCADS)
    237, 238

Short SC1 9, 11, 65, 76, 77,
    100
Showers, Bob 267
Side-force indicator 134
Sideways movement 134
Sidewinder 44, 47, 50, 52–54,
    56, 60, 236, 268
Simpson, Duncan 141
Sir Galahad 50
Six Day war 172
Ski Jump 46, 51, 237, 238,
    242, 250–4, 260
SkyHook 239–41
Smith, Lieutenant David 47,
    50
Smith, Larry 264
Sortie validation tests 172
Spanish Navy 258
Spare parts 170
Spey engine 109
Spinning trials 130–2
Spray-on landing pad 188
Stack, John 70, 71
Suhr, Captain V. 120
Super Sabre 181
Supersonic performance 101,
    110
Swept wing aerodynamics 15
Swivelling nozzles 8, 12, 18
Symington, Senator 164

Tactical Air Control Center
    191, 248
Target decay 191
Taylor, Lieutenant Commander
    Doug 250, 251
TF41 engine 167
Thomas, Lieutenant Steve 43,
    44
Thomson, Squadron Leader
    Tom Leckey 162
Throttle 24–25
Thrust and weight 65–66, 81
Titanium 230

Tonkinson, Barry 141
Townsend, Captain 'Doc' 218
Track-orientation 34
Transatlantic Air Race 173
Trident 109
Tripartite evaluation squadron
    112, 113, 115–28, 211
Tropical trials 139, 140
Trowern, Squadron Leader
    Fred 120
TSR2 6, 110, 111
Turbofan engine 22
Tyson, Lieutenant Commander
    J. J. 117, 120

Undercarriage 66, 85
Unplanned destination 35
U.S. Air Force 118
U.S. Army 118
U.S. Marine Corps 30–31, 32,
    38, 40, 117, 127, 147,
    149–79, 185, 244, 257,
    261
U.S. Navy 234, 245, 258

VAK-191 117–18, 128
Variable stability helicopter
    73
Vectored thrust 18, 21, 25, 28,
    101, 107, 112, 113,
    207–25, 255
Versatile Warrior 191
Vibration problems 227, 231,
    232
Vietnam war 39, 106, 152, 171
    172, 176–8, 203, 223

VIFF 208, 210–25
von Karman, Theodore 17,
    21–22
V/STOL 17, 21, 24, 25

Walwyn, Lieutenant-
    Commander Peter 54
Warner, John 171
Warning device 134–5
Warsaw Pact 181, 182, 195,
    198, 202
Weapons potential 189
Weapons System Evaluation
    Group (WESAG) 172
Weight and thrust 65–66, 81
Wibault, Michel 9
Williams, Major Drax 178,
    223, 224
Williamson, Air Vice Marshal
    Peter 162
Wilson, Harold 110
Wind tunnel tests 71, 209
Wright Field 18

XFV 12 262
XP 831 75, 79, 84, 85, 90,
    107, 113
XP 836 90, 94, 95
XS 688 125
XV 5 158
XV 276 145
XV 277 219

YAK-36 255
YAV-8B 269–71, 275, 276

Bruce Myles learned to fly as a teenager. He is a public relations consultant and a former BBC Television correspondent, and is the author of two other books published in Britain, America and Japan. He is married with two sons.

PHOTO CREDITS